# DINOSAURS, DUNES, AND DRIFTING CONTINENTS

## The Geohistory of the Connecticut Valley

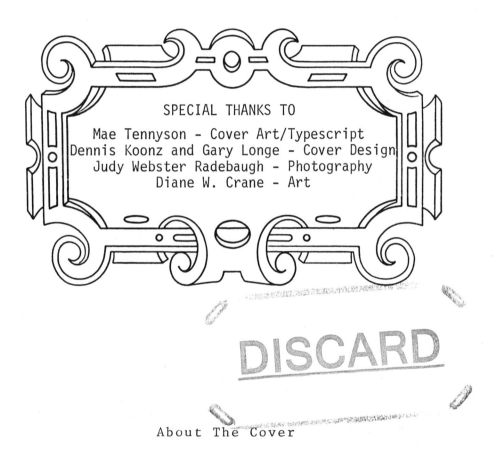

SPECIAL THANKS TO

Mae Tennyson - Cover Art/Typescript
Dennis Koonz and Gary Longe - Cover Design
Judy Webster Radebaugh - Photography
Diane W. Crane - Art

### About The Cover

Two hundred million years ago, a 9-foot-long herbivore, Anchisaurus, pauses before drinking at the edge of a shallow Connecticut Valley lake. In the foreground, a small, 3-foot-long carnivore, Podokesaurus, runs past in search of insects. The vegetation pictured includes a palm-like cycad tree and horsetail rushes along the lakeshore.

DINOSAURS, DUNES, AND DRIFTING CONTINENTS: the geohistory of the Connecticut Valley

Copyright © 1984, 1986  by Richard D. Little

ISBN  0-9616520-0-4

2nd Edition

Published by  c/o Richard D. Little
36 Plantation Circle
Greenfield, MA  01301

For Suzanne, with love.

# acknowledgements

The process of producing this book would have taken eons longer if not for the time made available by a sabbatical leave from Greenfield Community College during the spring semester, 1984.  A portion of the proceeds from this book will go to support educational pursuits at G.C.C.

Mae Tennyson was invaluable with her skills in typing, editing, paste-up, and design.  Tom Boisvert and Dennis Koonz provided graphical assistance.  I am indebted to Judy Webster Radebaugh for many hours of time and energy spent in the production of the photographs.  The Pratt Museum of Amherst College, Amherst, MA, allowed their extensive collection to be photographed.  Dr. John C. Holden graciously permitted the use of his artwork seen on page 1 and elsewhere.  Many other people helped in the creative process by offering advice, encouragement, and by answering questions.  To my wife, Suzanne, goes special thanks for her critical reading of the manuscript, substantial suggestions for its improvement, and support during what often seemed an unending project.  My children, Jason (age 11) and Merika (age 8), each contributed in their own way as some of the following pages attest.

The manuscript was read by the following reviewers whose time and comments were greatly appreciated.  I, however, take full responsibility for any errors or omissions.  Dr. Warren I. Johansson, Carolyn Boardman, Dennis Wilkins, Phyllis Nahman, Kathy Masalski, and Linda Shaughnessy.

COMMENTS?

CRITICISMS?

Please contact
the author at

36 Plantation Cir.
Greenfield, MA
01301

preface


It has been over 40 years since George Bain of Amherst College and Howard Meyerhoff of the University of Pennsylvania first published The Flow of Time in the Connecticut Valley, a "popular" account of the fascinating geologic events of our region. Many things have changed over the intervening decades, most notably, the acceptance of the idea of drifting continents. This book explains how the valley's development is intimately related to the movement of the earth's crustal plates, why valley rocks are different from the surrounding highlands, what ancient life and the environment of the valley were like, and how the present landscape developed. Resources and environmental problems are discussed as well as the geologic future.

The book is written with a minimum of technical terms and is extensively illustrated. References are included for those who wish an introduction to the voluminous technical literature. Appendix II lists addresses for more information as well as a newly compiled map showing geologic data availability for the valley and surrounding areas in Massachusetts and Connecticut.

Sketches of Mesozoic animals of the valley reproduced from R. S. Lull's "Triassic Life of the Connecticut Valley", Bulletin 81, Conn. Geological and Natural History Survey (1953), are included in Appendix III.

In short, this book provides an easily read but complete account of the exciting geology of our unique place in space and time.

# CONTENTS

ILLUSTRATIONS

# PART ONE

# INTRODUCTION

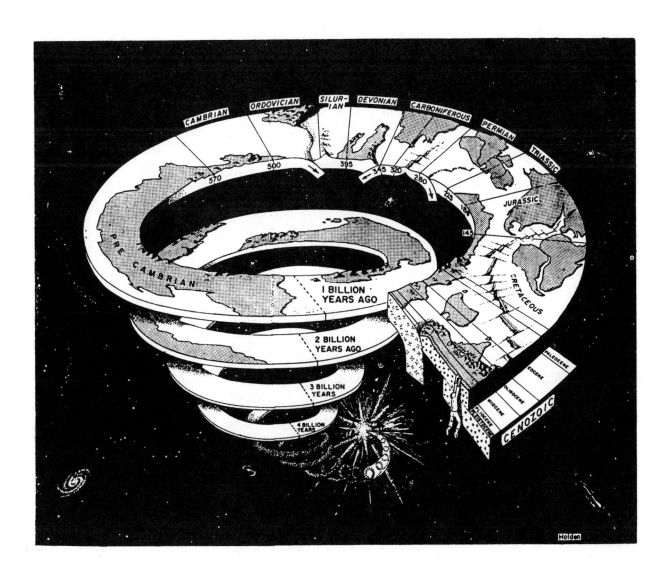

Figure 1 - Geologic time scale from the "Big Bang" to the
present.  Each whorl equals one billion years.
(Reprinted with permission of John C. Holden)

## UNIQUENESS of the CONNECTICUT VALLEY

Looking into the past, we can trace the geneology of the life and landscape of the Connecticut Valley back almost one billion years, into the Precambrian Era (Fig. 1). Oceans, mountains, earthquakes, dinosaurs, lava flows, glaciers, rivers, and people are all part of our geohistory. Our valley is a unique spot in New England, one of the few places in the world where such diverse history can be seen in so small a geographic area (Fig. 2).

The three variables used to evaluate the "quality" of landscapes, vividness, variety, and unity, are well-displayed in the Connecticut Valley. Spectacular lava ridges, inspiration for generations of artists, dissect productive valley floodplains from Greenfield, Massachusetts, to New Haven, Connecticut. Unifying the ecosystem, the river sometimes flows in sensuous meanders through velvet-green meadows, other times straight and fast through rocky gorges, or cascades over waterfalls, exhibiting incredible variety for a major river. It is the river's erosive force that has created the valley and surrounding hills, and provides hydropower and rich floodplain soils.

The beauty of our landscape, although superficially appreciated by many, is greatly enhanced by an awareness of our geological heritage. Rocks and landforms are great testimonials to our colorful past. Let us journey through the fourth dimension and experience "Dinosaurs, Dunes, and Drifting Continents," the exciting geohistory of the Connecticut Valley.

## ROCKS and HISTORY

Geologists are the ultimate earthly historians. About 4 1/2 billion years ago, our geological clock officially started as the earth cooled enough to allow lava to harden and become ancient earth crust.

To help realize the vastness of this time frame, consider the concept of one billion. How many years will it take for a billion seconds to pass? See Table 1 for the answer.

Figure 1 depicts a generalization of the history of the earth with the major time divisions. Note the tremendous amount of earth history in the Precambrian, before life became abundant. Homo sapiens, a very recent arrival, clings tenaciously to the present. John McPhee, in Basin and Range, views geotime this way:

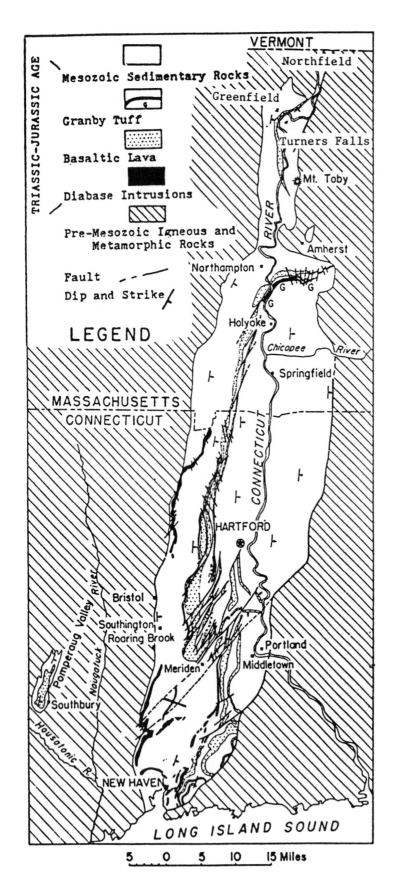

5  0  5  10  15 Miles

### TABLE 1

| ILLUSTRATING THE MAGNITUDE OF A BILLION |
| --- |
| HOW MANY YEARS IN ONE BILLION SECONDS? |
| One minute = 60 seconds |
| One hour   = 3,600 seconds |
| One day    = 86,400 seconds |
| One year   = 31,557,600 seconds |
| Dividing 1 billion seconds by 31,557,600 (seconds in one year) equals 31.69 years. |

Figure 2 - Geologic index map
of the Connecticut
Valley region.
(Modified from
Krynine, 1950).

"With your arms spread wide to represent all time on earth, look at one hand with its line of life. The Cambrian begins in the wrist, and the Permian Extinction is at the outer end of the palm. All of the Cenozoic is in a fingerprint, and in a single stroke with a medium-grained nail file, you could eradicate human history"[2] (Figures 3-a and 3-b).

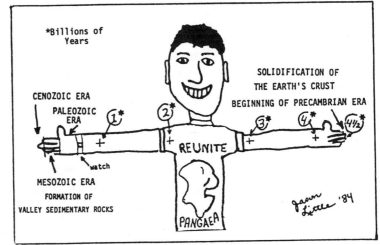

Figure 3-a.

Figure 3 - Geologic time on a "human" scale.

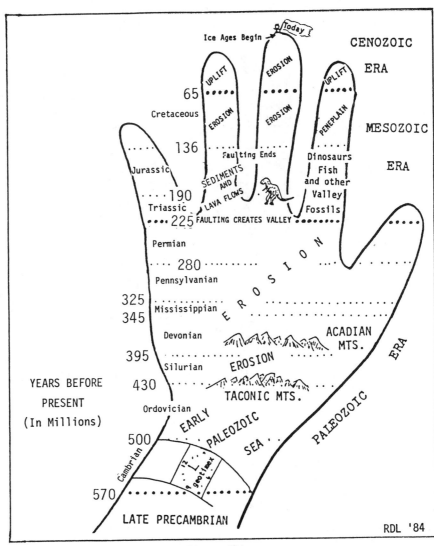

Figure 3-b.

6

Gazing into the depths of the Grand Canyon, even the most casual
tourist has some idea that there is meaning in those rocky layers. The
early chapters in the Grand Canyon history are at river level, 6,000
feet below the rim, with progressively younger events above (Fig. 4).
This relationship of time and the order of rock layers is known as
"superposition", and is essential in understanding earth history.

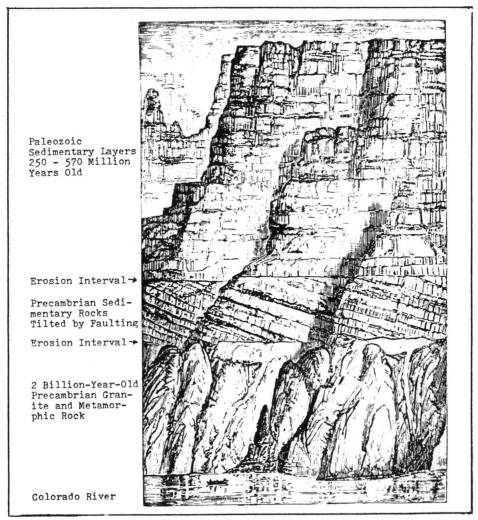

Paleozoic
Sedimentary Layers
250 - 570 Million
Years Old

Erosion Interval→

Precambrian Sedi-
mentary Rocks
Tilted by Faulting

Erosion Interval→

2 Billion-Year-Old
Precambrian Gran-
ite and Metamor-
phic Rock

Colorado River

Figure 4 - Superposition as illustrated in the Grand Canyon. (Drawing from
John Wesley Powell's exploration report, 1875).[3]

Although the Grand Canyon has a greater amount of time and diversity
of events recorded in the rocks, the Connecticut Valley has a thicker
sedimentary record which is much easier to study. Instead of cliff-
climbing to investigate the layers, our rocks are conveniently tilted
for viewing (Fig. 5). The tilt is courtesy of the Eastern Border Fault
which moved the formerly horizontal layers downward. Today, we can see
the oldest rocks to the west, becoming progressively younger to the east,
revealing an exciting sequence of events: lakes, rivers, floods, lava
flows, and, of course, dinosaurs!

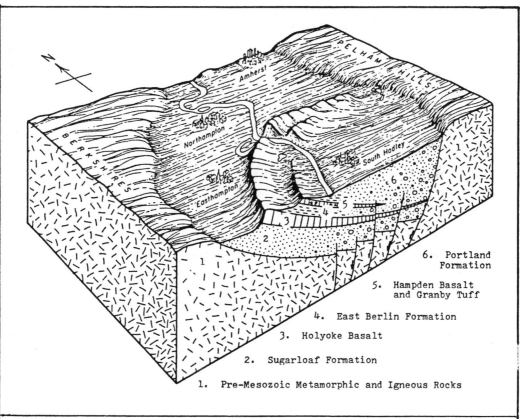

6. Portland
   Formation

5. Hampden Basalt
   and Granby Tuff

4. East Berlin Formation

3. Holyoke Basalt

2. Sugarloaf Formation

1. Pre-Mesozoic Metamorphic and Igneous Rocks

| FORMATION | AGE | DESCRIPTION |
|-----------|-----|-------------|
| 6. Portland | Lower Jurassic | Arkosic sandstone, siltstone, and shale. Fossil fish and dinoprints sometimes encountered. Approximately 4,000 feet thick. |
| 5. Hampden Basalt and Granby Tuff | Lower Jurassic (but younger than 4) | Thin basalt flows interbedded with fine-grained sediments and explosive volcanic deposits of ash and larger "bombs" (tuff). |
| 4. East Berlin | Lower Jurassic (but younger than 3) | Gray siltstone-shale reaching 1,500 feet thick. Fish fossils and dinoprints, such as at Dinosaur State Park in Rocky Hill, Conn. |
| 3. Holyoke Basalt | Lower Jurassic | Several lava flows of fine-grained, gray basalt totaling as much as 600 feet. Column joints common. |
| 2. Sugarloaf Arkose | Upper Triassic | Stream-deposited sandstone and conglomerate with poor sorting and many weak minerals (such as feldspar), indicating short distance of transport from nearby mountains. About 6,000 feet thick. Same as New Haven Arkose further south. |
| 1. "Basement Rock" | Late Precambrian to Mid-Paleozoic | Former ocean sedimentary layers and occasional lava and ash beds now metamorphosed and intruded by granite. Complex geology. |

Figure 5 - Block diagram of the geology of the northern Connecticut Valley with descriptions of the bedrock. (Block diagram modified from Tollo and Nicholson, 1979).

How do you date a dinosaur? (With great care!) While superposition tells us whether something is relatively older or younger, it
does not give us a numerical date. Dinosaur bones are much too old for
the 40,000 year range of radiocarbon dating. Fortunately, we have other
methods of radioactive dating. Lava, for example, has radioactive minerals which can be analyzed. The Holyoke Range and other valley ridges
contain lava flows (see Fig. 2) dated at approximately 190 million years
old. Since the dinosaur prints are found in sedimentary layers above
and below the lavas, they must also be about this age.

Besides "when?", "what happened?" is a major question geologists
ponder. The idea that rocks are historical documents is foreign to most
people, but with a little training, their secrets can be read.

Rocks originate in only three ways, and are recycled from one variety
to another as Figure 6 illustrates. We are very fortunate to have excellent examples of all three rock classes in the Connecticut Valley. Most
areas of New England are dominated by metamorphic rock with a sprinkling
of granite, which was formerly molten and pushed into the metamorphics.
However, our valley has a splendid sequence of sedimentary rocks and igneous lavas and intrusions, with the metamorphics and granite preserved
in the surrounding hills (see Fig. 5).

How this came to pass is considered next.

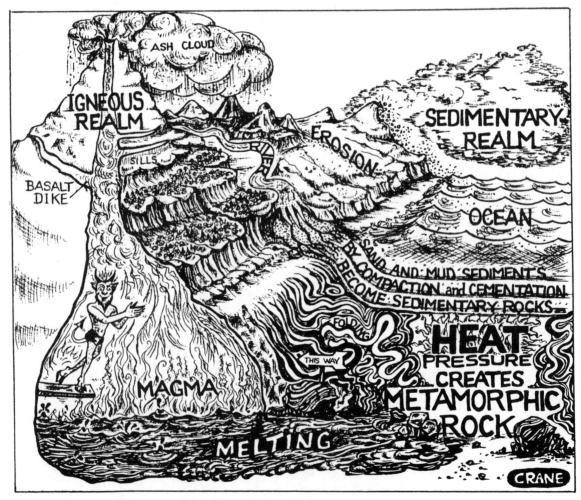

Figure 6 - The rock cycle. See Appendix I for identification
guide to valley rock types.

# PART TWO    the Paleozoic Era

## from SEA to SUPERCONTINENT

## DRIFTING CONTINENTS

Since the 1960s, abundant evidence has been gathered to support the revolutionary idea that the earth's crust is very mobile, able to move at rates of inches per year.  While this seems small, given time, such movement can create tremendous changes in the earth's geography. Lateral motion along California's infamous San Andreas fault will slide Los Angeles adjacent to San Francisco in about 25 million years; add another 50 million and Los Angeles, coastal Southern California, and Baja California will be a new addition to the State of Alaska!  Even here in the Connecticut Valley, our rocks and landscape are monuments to wandering crustal "plates" which have both collided and split apart over the past 600 million years.

The solid crust of the earth is broken into a series of plates (Fig. 7), which move relative to each other.  Drifting plates slip on a soft zone in the upper mantle, probably propelled by heat (convection) currents (Fig. 8).  Similar motions can be seen in any pot of hot soup (tomato rice is highly recommended) with cracker crumbs on top for clarity.  As areas above rising heat currents diverge, cooler regions converge making mini-mountain zones of cracker crumbs.

The idea that continents are drifting like dumplings in a stew may be hard to swallow, but realize that our crust is very thin compared to the inner earth.  If we dig a vertical tunnel in our valley to reach the center of the earth, we will find that the first 18 miles are solid crustal rock, the next 1800 miles are hot, semi-solid mantle rocks, followed by 2000 miles of core, molten in the outer parts, solid at the center.

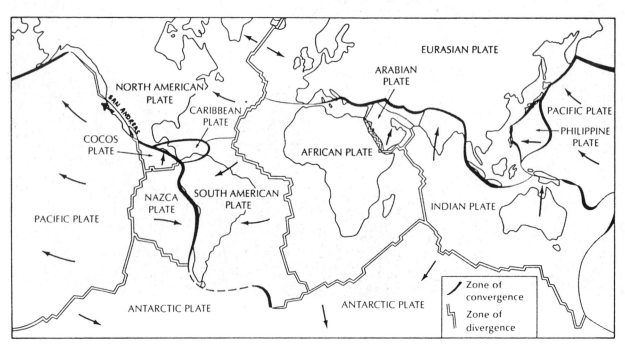

Figure 7 - Major plates of the earth's crust and their
directions of movement.[1]

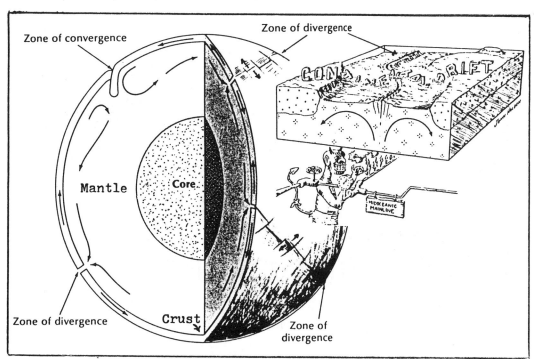

Figure 8 - Earth structure showing mantle convection currents and crustal drift.
(Modified from Larsen and Birkeland, 1982, p. 704).[1]  Inset illustrates
possible cause of mantle convection and continental drift.
(Courtesy of John C. Holden).


Eighteen miles of solid crust sits on 3800 miles of unstable mantle and
core.  If the earth were scaled down to the size of an egg, the egg
shell would be more than twice the thickness of the crust.  Our crust
is an unstable foundation.  North America is currently drifting away
from Europe, widening the Atlantic Ocean by one inch per year, with some
small Pacific Ocean crustal plates moving up to 20 times faster.  So
much for "terra firma".

Oceans form as plates separate, a process currently operating in
the Atlantic (see Fig. 7).  A prominent crack develops as plates diverge, allowing magma to flow upwards creating the volcanoes and lava
flows of the ocean crust.  Iceland, located on our Atlantic Ocean
"crack", is a great observation platform from which to study seafloor
spreading in the comfort of dry land, rather than under 10,000 feet of
cold ocean.

Converging plates cause the world's most spectacular scenery and
awesome disasters.  Continental collisions, such as India's continuing
impact with Eurasia, produce the earth's greatest mountains, the Hima-
layas, which are complexly folded and faulted rocks.  A more common
type of convergence occurs where thin ocean crust "dives" under thick
continental crust.  These Subduction Zones (Fig. 9) are noted for their
numerous deadly earthquakes and picturesque but explosive volcanoes.
Subduction occurs all around the Pacific creating such landmarks as
Mt. St. Helens, Crater Lake, Mt. Fuji, El Chichon (Mexico), and the
Andes Mountains.

12

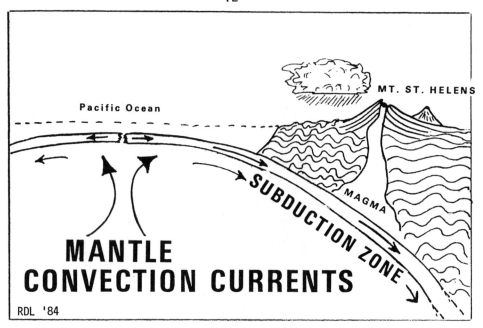

Figure 9 - Subduction zone of the Pacific Northwest.

## OLD SEAS and SEDIMENTS

Beginning at the Paleozoic wrist of time (see Fig. 3) almost
600 million years ago, a warm, shallow sea covered much of the United
States.  Corals, clam-like brachiopods, mud-crawling trilobites, and
sea scorpions (eurypterids) were some of the inhabitants of the early
Paleozoic Proto-Atlantic (Fig. 10).  Their remains can be collected
today in nearby eastern New York and western Vermont.  However, the
heat and pressure of subsequent metamorphic events have destroyed the
clues to ancient oceans in New England except in a few rare places.
The marble of the Cambrian-Lower Ordovician Stockbridge Formation,
seen in the white outcrops and quarries of western Massachusetts and
Connecticut, contains some fossils (bryozoa, cup corals).  North of
Greenfield in Bernardston, distorted remains of crinoid stems (sea
lilies), brachiopods, and corals of early Silurian age have been
found.  Slate quarries of nearby Guilford, Vermont, occasionally reveal the tiny, saw-blade shapes of Silurian Graptolites, small floating animals now extinct.

Our tropical sealife is not surprising since geographically, we
were in a position similar to Brazil, about 20° south of the equator
and tilted as Figure 11 illustrates.  Accurate ancient latitude information comes from the analysis of rock magnetism.  Many fine-grained
sedimentary rocks and lavas have magnetic minerals that act like com-
pas needles, inclined toward the ancient poles.  By measuring this

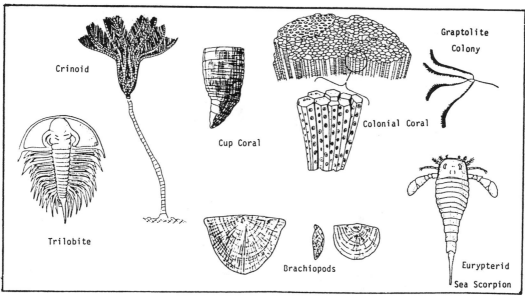

Figure 10 - Lower Paleozoic fossils mentioned in text.

inclination, the latitude when the rock was formed can be determined.

Exploding volcanoes during the Ordovician herald the beginning of the end for the Proto-Atlantic Ocean.  A subduction zone (Fig. 12) develops several hundred miles eastward of the continental margin, creating a magnificient island chain of tall strato-type volcanoes, similar to Mt. St. Helens.  Erosion of the volcanoes floods the surrounding sea floor with layers of sand, mud, and ash from explosive eruptions.  Coral animals built beautiful fringing reefs around the islands 50 million years before sharks or other fish swam the oceans.  This tropical paradise, known as the Bronson Hill Plate and located somewhere between the plates of Laurentia and Baltica, is the ancestral bedrock of the Connecticut Valley.

## TACONIC MOUNTAIN BUILDING

Subduction zones indicate crustal convergence.  The Bronson Hill Plate's volcanoes and reefs collide with the eastern margin of Laurentia, forming the complexly faulted and folded Taconic Mountains (Fig. 13).  As erosion attacked these 10,000 foot peaks, a flood of sediment washed into the adjacent shallow ocean.  This wedge-shaped pile of gravel and mud, known as the Queenston Delta, is 4000 feet thick near the former mountain front and tapers to a feather edge of shale 500 miles to the west in Michigan.

As the Taconics eroded, shallow Silurian and Devonian seas reclaimed the eastern seaboard leaving behind shell-rich layers of limestone and dolomite now seen in the rim rock of Niagara Falls, the Helderberg Cliffs

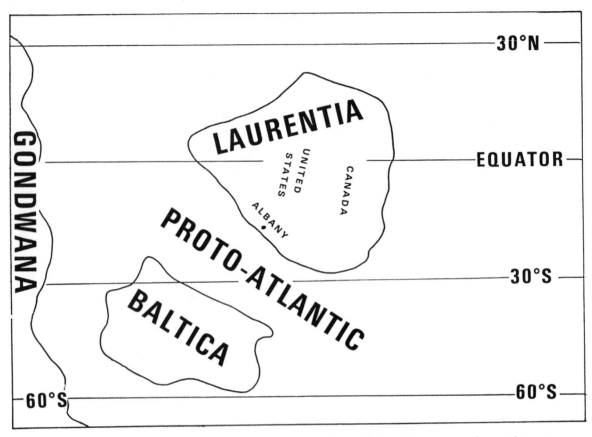

Figure 11 - Paleogeography of the Cambrian Period. Albany, N.Y., was located near the shoreline of Laurentia. (Adapted from Scotese et al, 1979).[2]

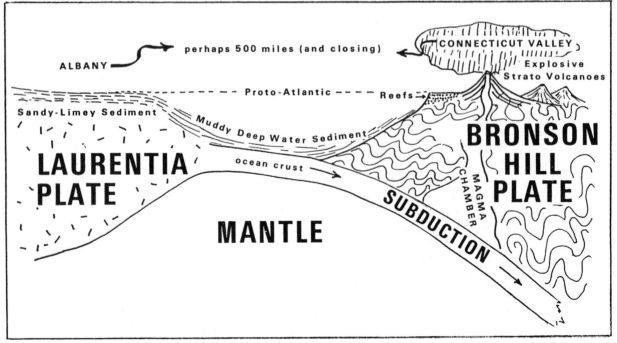

Figure 12 - Early Ordovician geography and plate tectonics of the Connecticut Valley region. (Based on Robinson and Hall, 1980).[3]

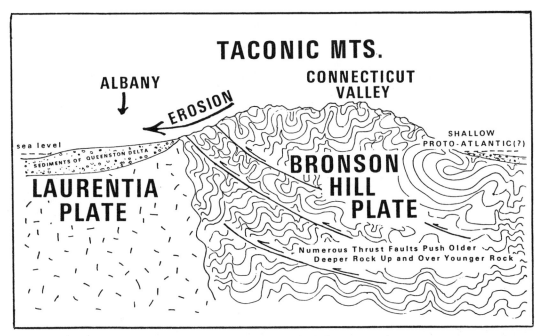

Figure 13 - Late Ordovician Paleogeography.

of Thatcher State Park west of Albany, New York, and the limey remains in Bernardston, Massachusetts. Shoreline sands and gravels of the advancing Silurian sea are found today in the hills east of our valley, capped by the resistant, quartz-rich Clough (pronounced "kluff") Formation. Heat and pressure of subsequent mountain-building events have fused the beach sands into quartzite and stretched the round quartz beach pebbles into the shapes of hotdogs and pencils. The ocean's stay was brief, since on the horizon appeared a continent destined to end the Proto-Atlantic's 300-million-year history.

## APPALACHIAN REVOLUTION

The mid-Paleozoic Devonian Period, the beginning of fish evolution, marks the start of the earth's most impressive land sculpting event. Due to drifting continents, Baltica collided with Maine and Canada. Gondwana (the great Southern Continental "conglomerate" of South America, Africa, India, Antarctica, and Australia) followed close behind to impact the remaining eastern portion of the United States (Fig. 14).

Imagine the forces involved as these massive earth-plates converged. The continental margins which had collected thousands of feet of sedimentary layers were the first areas to be affected. The folding, faulting, metamorphism, and rock-melting of this period produced the most complicated geology in New England. Unraveling the history of this mixed-up assemblage requires patience, perseverance, and a good imagination.

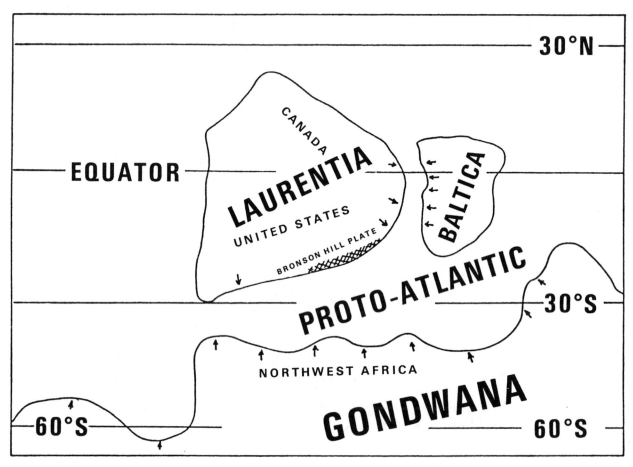

Figure 14 - Mid-Silurian paleogeography. (Adapted from Scotese et al, 1979)?

Glacial deposits, erosion, rock-melting, and hammer-swinging "rock hounds" have all served to frustrate geological detectives in New England. Bouldery glacial debris hides bedrock; erosion has erased more than 10 miles of the overlying rock record; melting during mountain building has destroyed the original rock structure of many parts of New England (but has created beautiful granites); and amateur geologists with a hammer-blow have at times obliterated minerals and delicate fold structures etched by thousands of years of weathering.  In spite of this, the major events which built the New England Appalachians (known as the Acadian Mountains) seem to fit into three stages.

Stage I:  Nappes.  Nappes (from the French word "tablecloth") are great folds that have been bent laterally as Figure 15-A illustrates.  From the east, drifting plates approached the sedimentary layers of our continental margin, producing a series of folds which were pushed, one over the other, tens of miles westward, inland toward safer ground, away from the advancing continents. Slip on a loose rug and similar patterns emerge.  The "pressure cooking" of metamorphism began to change the rocks into gneiss, schist, and slate.

Stage II:  Backfolding.  The nappes were then uplifted and pushed eastward, squeezed out of the way as the collision progressed (Fig. 15-B and Fig. 15-C).  Maximum metamorphic conditions occurred as temperatures reached 1200°F accompanied by pressures equal to about 14 miles of overlying rock, creating "high grade" metamorphic minerals such as sillimanite, garnet, and cordierite.  High pressure fracturing, called cataclasis, cracked minerals and rocks.  Some rocks melted, intruding neighboring formations, and are known as "plutons" after the god of Hell, Pluto.

Stage III.  Gneiss Domes.  Folding continued, accompanied by an upward flowage of deep-seated mushy (not molten) gneiss rocks that pushed overlying rocks up and out of their way (Fig. 15-D). The gneiss domes occurred because of a density adjustment.  They were slightly lighter than the cooler, overlying layers and tended to move upward through them.  The gneiss domes and plutons of the Connecticut Valley region are shown in Figure 16.

By the end of the Devonian, after 40 to 50 million years of literal upheaval, the Acadian portion of the Appalachian chain was completed as Europe (Baltica) and Africa (northwest Gondwana) became "welded" to North America.  To the south, geologic unrest continued through the late Paleozoic as Gondwanaland continued to impact, creating the Central and Southern Appalachians stretching from Pennsylvania to Alabama, and the Ouachitas in Arkansas and eastern Oklahoma.

Erosion of the mountains began and, similar to the Taconic's fate, the Appalachians were recycled as a great delta (Fig. 17). Today, the high Devonian Appalachians can be seen in the pieces of gravel, sand, and mud, now sedimentary rock, of the Catskills.

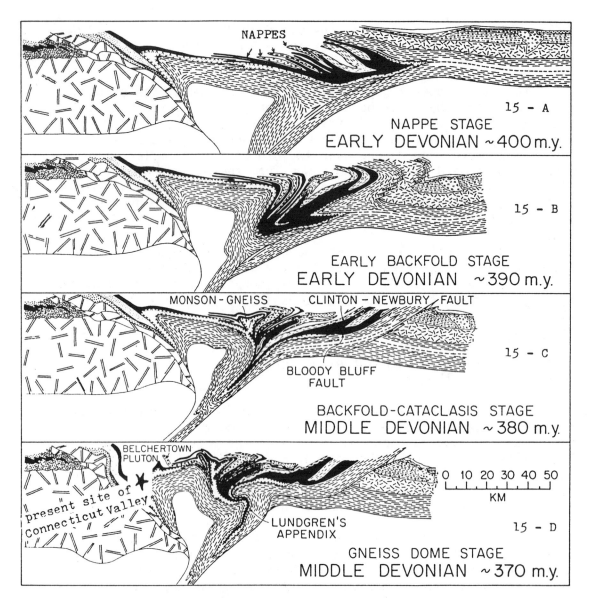

Figure 15 - Stages in the development of the Northern Appalachian
Mountains. These events are diagrammed as they took
place about 5-20 miles deep within the earth. Note
the star indicating position of the Connecticut Valley.
(From Robinson and Hall, 1980).[3]

    While the details of Appalachian plate tectonics will continue
to be debated and refined, the end result is a profound revolution
in world geography.  The Proto-Atlantic died, great mountains rose,
and the world became unified as the supercontinent of Pangaea
(Fig. 18).

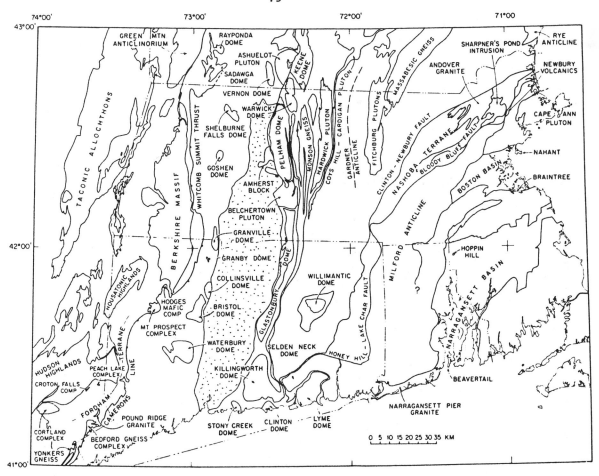

Figure 16 - Geologic structure map of Southern New England showing
domes and the Mesozoic Connecticut Valley (dotted).
(From Robinson and Hall, 1980).[3]

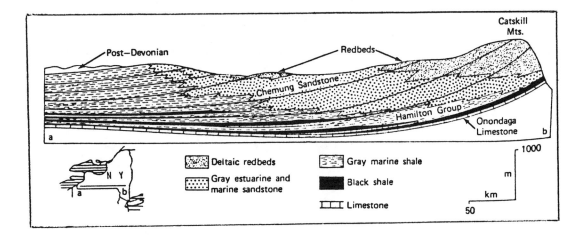

Figure 17 - Cross section of the Catskill Delta. (From Stearn, et al,
1979).[4]

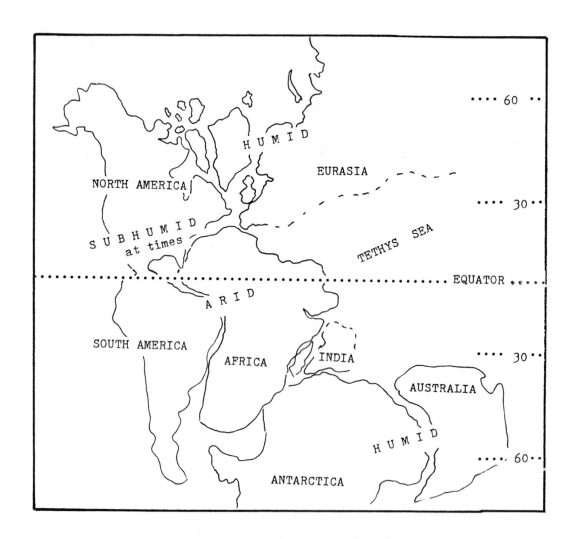

Figure 18 - Pangaea with early Mesozoic climate patterns. (Modified
from Hubert et al, 1978)[5]

# PART THREE    The Mesozoic Era

# CREATION and DESTRUCTION of the VALLEY

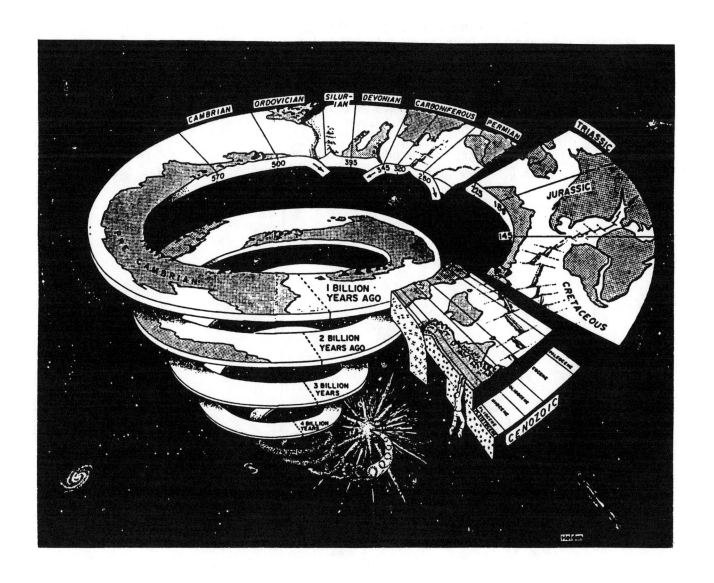

22

# CREATION

The Late Paleozoic found us situated in the mountainous middle of Pangaea enduring eons of erosion as rushing rivers flattened the landscape.  However, all was not quiet in the region.  Earthquakes shook Central Pangaea as bedrock bent downward forming the Narragansett Basin of southeastern Massachusetts and Rhode Island.  Pennsylvanian-age plants flourished and formed coal layers in this land-locked basin as well as in the great coastal swamps of Pennsylvania and West Virginia. Later, metamorphism and some igneous intrusions transformed Narragansett coal to meta-anthracite and graphite, greatly reducing its combustability.

Even a supercontinent is not stable on our churning earth.  As the Mesozoic begins, Pangaea stretches and cracks, "labor pains" of the soon-to-be-born Atlantic Ocean.  The break does not follow previous continental boundaries, and North America benefits in acreage at the expense of Europe and Africa.  Rock zones from Newfoundland through the Carolinas have definite similarities to Europe and Africa, including trilobite fossils of Paleozoic age.

The stretching stresses produced picturesque down-faulted valleys ("normal" faults) which are completely different from the thrust faults

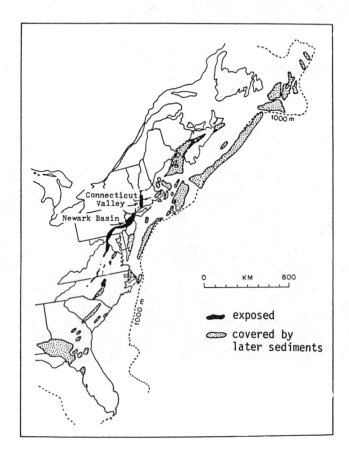

Figure 19 - Mesozoic fault-basins along eastern North America. Dotted line indicates approximate edge of continent below sea level. (From Hubert, 1978).[1]

developed during the Taconic and Appalachian collisions. Besides the Connecticut Valley, these fault-basins are found from the Grand Banks to Florida (Fig. 19), and even across the Atlantic in Morocco. Similar to the landscape of California's Death Valley, but with more moisture, these valleys were bounded on one side by moderately high, steep-sided mountains having prominent river canyons. Ferns and coniferous forests, lakes with abundant fish, and roving reptiles and amphibians added excitement to this beautiful landscape (Fig. 20).

The Eastern Border Fault, creator of the Connecticut Valley, has been inactive for 140 million years, yet it must have been an impressive cliff during much of the early Mesozoic. For 85 million years, sporadic earthquakes lowered the valley and raised the eastern hills. The estimated total vertical offset along the fault zone ranges from 15,000 feet in Massachusetts to as much as 35,000 feet in Connecticut, where the valley is wider and deeper.[2] Of course, erosion constantly attacked the rising hills, resulting in accumulations of up to 16,000 feet of sedimentary rock in today's valley. These sedimentary layers provide the geologic clues to the exciting events of the Age of Dinosaurs.

Today, the sedimentary basin of the Connecticut Valley stretches over 100 miles from Northfield, Massachusetts, to New Haven, Connecticut (see Fig. 2), with an average width of 17 miles, but the Mesozoic Valley of 200 million years ago must have been significantly larger. The valley-forming Eastern Border Fault begins an unknown distance south of New Haven, where it is covered by sediments and sea water and can be traced for 130 miles north to Keene, New Hampshire. The former valley deposits between Northfield and Keene were thin and have been lost to erosion. The eastern valley edge is well-marked since the Border Fault forms the boundary between the resistant metamorphic rocks of the Eastern Highlands and the weaker sedimentary rocks of the valley. Residents of the western portion of the valley will be surprised to learn that the valley extended much farther to the west, perhaps linking us with the Newark Basin (see Fig. 19). However, recent analysis of the origin of river-transported sediments indicates that these basins probably remained isolated.[3] From their sources in the Eastern Highlands, our valley rivers flowed west and southwest, across alluvial fans, floodplains, and old lake beds (Fig. 21). They journeyed beyond present valley limits to drain into the newly opening Atlantic Sea.

## SEDIMENTARY ROCKS and LANDFORMS

Bain and Meyerhoff, in The Flow of Time in the Connecticut Valley, describe our colorful valley rocks as an "inlay" in the mosaic of central Massachusetts. The Eastern Border Fault's cut into the complex bedrock mosaic starts the inlay. Sediments washed into the "cut", bringing shades of brown and layered, fragmental textures that were strikingly different from the surrounding hills.

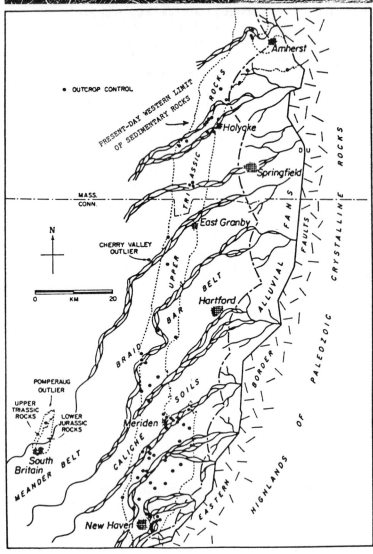

Figure 20 - On the shore of a Mesozoic Connecticut Valley lake. In the early morning, the 7m phytosaur *Rutiodon* snatches a *Semionotus* from the shallows. The tall horsetail *Equisetum* and cycad *Otozamites* thrive in the wet mud of the lake strand. Stands of the conifer *Araucarioxylon* tower 60m high along the distant horizon on sandy soils of the well-drained uplands. The cliff results from movement along the Eastern Border Fault. The dinosaur *Eubrontes* passed this way the previous evening. (From Hubert et al, 1978. Drawing by Amy Hubert).[1]

Figure 21 - Generalized trends of valley rivers in Late Triassic time. (From Hubert et al, 1978).[1]

Canyon-cutting rivers disgorge their coarse gravels on the valley floor creating alluvial fans along the faulted valley boundary (Fig. 22). Rough-edged and jumbled mud flow deposits, indicative of semi-arid conditions, were common among the fans' stream-rounded gravels. Lakeshores and floodplains rimmed the fans with their finer-grained sediments and gentler slopes.

Mt. Warner and Amherst, on a block of Paleozoic metamorphic bedrock, stood above the fans as a barrier separating the Mesozoic Connecticut Valley into two sections: the Deerfield Basin to the north and the Hartford Basin to the south (see Fig. 2).

Lakes, some as large as Utah's Great Salt Lake, were spectacular features of our valley. Depending upon prevailing climatic conditions, their shorelines expanded or dried to salt flats, leaving telltale impressions of now-dissolved salt and gypsum crystals, dead fish, and dinosaur footprints. Deeper lake floor beds, deposited under oxygen-poor conditions, are easy to spot. Look for black shale beds among the red sedimentary layers (Fig. 23).

Warm winds from the west and northwest created waves and lake currents that shaped soft sediment into wavy ripple marks. Mud flats of the drying lakes and floodplains exhibit structures such as mud cracks (some as much as two feet deep), rain and hail craters, trails and burrows due to worms, insects, and crustaceans, and last but certainly not least, dinoprints (Fig. 24).

Our valley had excellent conditions for the preservation of footprints but was a poor host for bones. Dinosaurs, drawn to drying lakes like

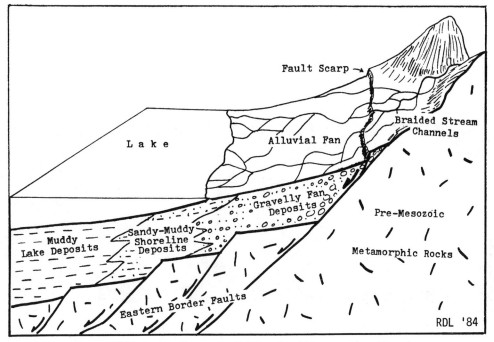

Figure 22 - Early Mesozoic Valley landforms and sediments.

b

c

a     Photo by David Hall

Figure 23 - Valley sedimentary features.  23-a - Black, organic-rich, lake-bottom
deposit, I-91 roadcut, Holyoke, MA.  23-b - Linear holes of now-dissolved gypsum crystals, formed by drying of lake water rich in sulfur
and calcium.  Two gypsum pieces have been fitted into holes.  Width of
view, 6 inches.  23-c - Sand casts of dissolved salt crystals formed
by drying salt lakes.  Width of view, 4 inches.

a                                    b

Figure 24 - Valley sedimentary structures.  24-a - Raindrop impressions.  Rock width,
4 inches.  24-b - Mud cracks, now filled with sand.  Rock width, 14 inches.

African elephants to waterholes, left their prints in fine-grained mud
to dry and harden, prepared for the next rainfall's protective cover
of sediment. Bones, even if buried, would decay in the oxygen-rich,
dry soil. While well over 30,000 prints have been found in the Connecticut Valley, only a few dozen bones and several partial skeletons have
been discovered. Two thousand miles away, wetter climate conditions
resulted in the preservation of countless bones buried in river sand
bars and deltas. While Utah's Dinosaur National Monument is justly proud of
its bones, the Connecticut Valley has the world's best display of dinoprints.

Earthquakes frequently shook the land as the border fault released
stress created by the splitting continent. Unstable clay-rich sediment
of the lakeshores slid into deeper parts of the lakes, creating many
strange features such as flow rolls, slump folds, and sediment breccias
and, on a larger scale, tilted the flat-lying layers downward toward
the eastern fault (see Fig. 25). Into the quake-cracked rocks seeped
mineral-rich fluids containing copper, barium, lead, and even small
amounts of silver and uranium. The mineralization is linked to the
arrival of molten rock in our valley. Hot springs, rising along
fault pathways, flushed minerals upward, and surface weathering of

Figure 25 - Sedimentary structures. 25-a - Flow Rolls, Sunderland, MA. "Jelly-
roll"-like features formed as cohesive sandy-muddy layers rolled
downslope. 25-b - Slump Folds formed by lake bottom clay layers
slipping into deeper portions of the lake. Rock is 9 inches wide.
25-c - Tilted sedimentary layers, Gill, MA.

lava also provided minerals to the ground water system. Copper, silver, and some uranium have been found at Newgate Prison, Connecticut, and barium and lead ore are collectors' items at long-abandoned mine sites in Loudville, Hatfield, and Leverett, Massachusetts.

Red rock or "brownstone", trademark of today's valley, would not have been seen by the dinosaurs. Their footprints were impressed in yellow-brown soils according to the microscopic analyses of John Hubert and colleagues at the University of Massachusetts. Yellow-brown limonite coatings on the sediment grains have been chemically altered to rusty red hematite during millions of years of burial. The two major processes involved are 1) the dissolving of iron-rich minerals by ground water, followed by redeposition as hematite cement in the pore spaces between grains, and, 2) transformation of limonite to hematite as the sedimentary layers dried.

> "Little I ask; my wants are few;
>     I only wish a hut of stone
> (A very plain brown stone will do),
>     That I may call my own;
> And close at hand is such a one,
>     In yonder street that faces the sun."

Oliver Wendell Holmes, "Contentment"

From door jambs to church steeples to row house apartments, much of southern New England and New York's nineteenth century architecture is constructed with our brownstone bedrock. Quarrying peaked in the late 1800s resulting in many now-flooded holes, some as deep as 300 feet.

The stone is a product of flash floods along semi-desert streams. Flood waters rushed across the alluvial fans spreading sheets of sand over the adjacent valley flats. The stacked sand layers average one foot per flood, but "superflood" deposits of over five feet have been measured. Imagine the many moments of sheer terror recorded in those stately building blocks!

Durability of the stone is provided by the type of cement bonding the grains together. The major lithifying agent in the Connecticut Valley is a feldspar mineral, albite, not commonly found as a sedimentary cement. Apparently the chemistry of the ground water, the cement transporter, was influenced by concentrations of albite in the alkaline waters of drying lakes. Albite, along with smaller amounts of quartz, dolomite, and iron provides permanence to the once-shifting sands.

In 1877, Turners Falls construction workers must have been puzzled by strange round shapes in rock they were quarrying for foundation stone for a now-dismantled bridge across the Connecticut (Fig. 26). Over 100 years would pass before these rare sedimentary structures, known as armored mud balls, would be officially recognized.[5] Formation of armored mud balls begins along stream cut banks as hard, dry mud blocks fall into the stream. Tumbling by the current

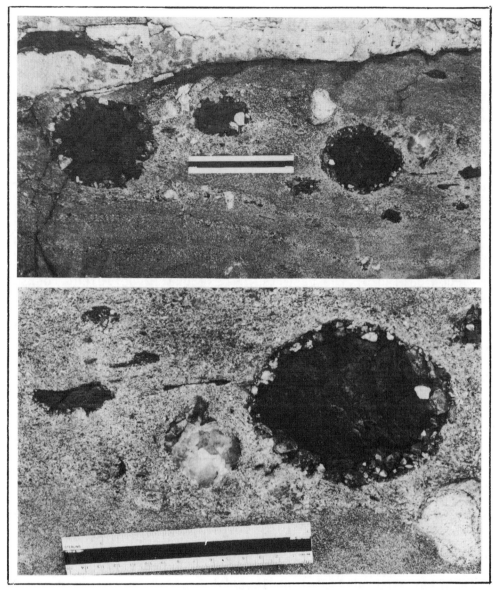

Figure 26 - Armored mud balls of the Lower Jurassic Turners Falls sandstone
preserved in bridge foundation stones, now at Greenfield Community College.  Ruler is 6 inches.  Photos by David Green.

rounds and softens the outer edge of the mud, making it sticky enough
to pick up pebbles from the stream bed, forming the "armor".  It is
essential for the armored mud balls to be rapidly covered before drying disintegrates them.  Armored mud balls, preserved in bedrock, have
been found in only eight other locations in the world, all shoreline
deposits.  Many of these sites have probably been destroyed by erosion
due to the poorly consolidated nature of the enclosing bedrock.  The
Turners Falls armored mud balls are unique.  They are the only stream-
formed armored mud balls preserved in the sedimentary rock record.
Today, they can be seen in the monumental samples preserved in Greenfield Community College's "Rock Park" and occasionally in the sand-
stone-conglomerate bedrock below the Turners Falls Dam.  Did dinosaurs
pause to ponder these strange rolling balls of mud?

# VOLCANISM in the VALLEY

The valley would be a dull place without our volcanics. Besides
their exciting origin, these tilted basalt flows and intrusions (see
Fig. 2) form prominent landscape ridges, bringing ecological diversity
to the floodplained lowlands. "Trap rock", as the basalt is commonly
called, comes from the Swedish word for step. Sweden has outcroppings
of lava layers which look like a landscape "stairway".

Volcanic activity greatly improved the Mesozoic environment. Lava
flows dammed stream channels, creating lakes that increased water sources
for plants, fish, and reptiles, and provided abundant mud flats for
footprints.

Quake-shattered fault zones of the splitting continent provided
pathways for magma to seep toward the surface for 25 million years,
between 171 and 196 million years ago according to radioactive po-
tassium-argon dating of the basalts.[6] These quartz-deficient rocks,
similar to lavas of Iceland and Hawaii, have a much different eruption
style from the explosive subduction volcanics seen here during Taconic
times, and presently at Mt. St. Helens and other Pacific margin volcanoes.

Add flour or cornstarch to boiling gravy and it becomes much thicker,
producing explosive bubbles as trapped gasses build up pressure to escape.
Quartz is nature's thickener for volcanic "gravy", and the results of this
recipe can be seen at Mt. St. Helens! Our Connecticut Valley basalt, being
low in quartz, did not explode but "oozed" from the faults. Stampeding
reptiles could have easily outrun the advancing "fissure flows" which
blanketed the landscape with up to several hundred feet of molten rock
at a time.

The Holyoke Range, our major monument to volcanic activity, is a
series of flows, ash, and interbedded sediments (see Fig. 5). Its
foundation is two flows of Holyoke Basalt, 320 and 255 feet thick. Major
source vents were located northwest of Mt. Hitchcock (Fig. 27). A small
vent, with five hundred-foot-long lava "dribbles" draped over its edge,
was revealed during construction of Route 91 near Mountain Park and is
preserved in the north lane road cut.[7] Moderate explosive activity followed the Holyoke flows as erupting cinder cones spread volcanic ash
(known as the Granby Tuff) over the landscape. The most violent activity occurred northeast of Mountain Park at Smith's Ferry where explosions
transported blocks of lava reaching lengths of 1 to 3 feet.

Figure 28 displays the ancient environment of the northern
valley area. The Deerfield lavas, up to 400 feet thick and tilted
by faulting, today form the bedrock of Greenfield's scenic Poet Seat
and the central portion of the Pocumtuck Range overlooking Old
Deerfield.

Strange and rarely seen pillow lavas were created as molten rock
met the water of shallow lakes. Pillows formed as lava squeezed through

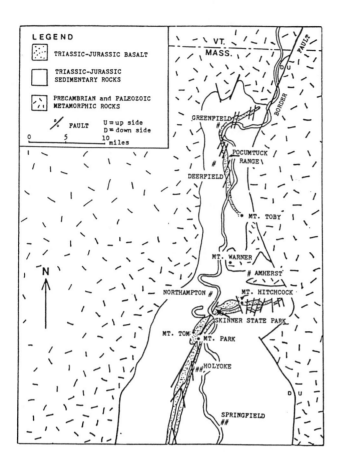

LEGEND

TRIASSIC-JURASSIC BASALT

TRIASSIC-JURASSIC
SEDIMENTARY ROCKS

PRECAMBRIAN and PALEOZOIC
METAMORPHIC ROCKS

FAULT    U = up side
         D = down side

0    5    10
              miles

Figure 27 - Northern Connecticut
Valley locations map.
(Modified from Tollo
and Nicholson, 1979).[9]

the water-chilled outer margin of the flow (Fig. 29). The unique sights and sounds of pillows forming as lava flowed under the sea in Hawaii has been filmed by diving geologists.[8]

Mud and sand can commonly be found squeezed up into the lower parts of the flows. Gasses, trapped by the hardening lava, formed holes called vesicles. These holes are commonly filled with minerals (mainly quartz, calcite, and prehnite) precipitated from groundwater during the past 190 million years. Elongated "pipestem" vesicles sometimes were pushed and tilted by the still-flowing lava, recording ancient flow directions. Occasionally, as lava advanced over wet mud, one to eight inch half-moon shaped bubbles were created. Bubbles, rising toward the ropey "pahoehoe" flow surface, create a vesicular zone marking the flow top; they are now used to distinguish between closely spaced flows.

Long lava tube caves, commonly found in volcanic areas, provided habitats for small reptiles. These now-collapsed features (Fig. 30) can occasionally be recognized as zones of fragments (breccia), some-times mineralized. The best documented former lava tube is King Phillip's Cave, located in the middle of the basalts of Talcott Mountain State Park,

Figure 28 - Block diagram of the northern Connecticut Valley during Triassic-Jurassic volcanism. Cinder cone volcanoes are usually less than 1000' high. The enlarged section shows vesicles (gas bubbles) tilted by flow.

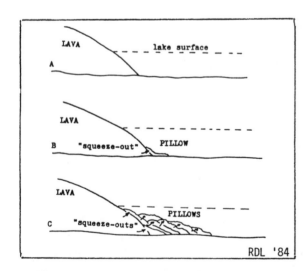

Figure 29 - Formation of pillow lavas.

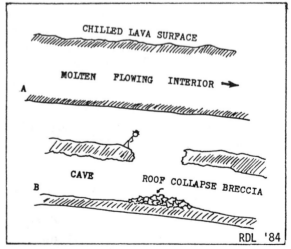

Figure 30 - Formation of lava tube cave.

about 20 miles west of Hartford.  The roof of the original lava tube
collapsed, forming a breccia zone, which was covered by a later flow.
Recent erosion has removed part of the breccia zone, exhuming the cave.

Cooling of lava produces polygonal shrinkage cracks, similar to
those of drying mud (Fig. 31).  Erosion along the cracks reveals striking five- and six-sided columnar forms, spectacularly displayed at
Devils Postpile National Monument, California, and Devils Tower, Wyo-
ming, as well as in the Holyoke Range's Titans Piazza (near the en-
trance to Skinner State Park), and at other locations.  The largest
valley columns are at Rabbit (or Peter's) Rock near New Haven, where
3- to 4-foot diameter columns can be seen.  Three-foot diameter columns
have been observed in the Deerfield lavas and in the shallow Barn Door
intrusions seen on Manitook Mountain, Suffield, Connecticut.  The columns
are best developed near the base of the flow units, where cooling was
slower.  The "precracked" nature of the hard basalt makes it ideal for
crushed stone, and many quarries are found throughout the valley sending
angular fragments to bolster railroad tracks and highway beds.

As the final puffs of ash drifted from volcanic vents, sediments
covered the flows as the valley continued to fill with the erosional
castoffs of eastern highlands.  Faulting continued, but this did not
daunt the dinosaurs, who invaded the valley in increasing numbers.

Figure 31 - Basalt lava columns, Cheapside Quarry, Deerfield, MA.  Columns are
approximately 3 feet in diameter.

## DINOSAURS and other VALLEY INHABITANTS

Native Americans, astute observers of nature, must have noticed
bird-like foot impressions in stone such as Pliny Moody unearthed in
his father's field in 1802.  No legend records their discovery, but
at the Moody's South Hadley farm, the tracks of "Noah's Raven" became
a door step, and others were quarried and displayed, gaining local no-
toriety (Fig. 32).  The world's first official documentation of
fossil footprints came 26 years later from Scotland when Henry Duncan,
clergyman and amateur naturalist, published an account of dinosaur
prints, which he thought were turtle tracks.

Figure 32 - "The Moody Foot Mark Quarry, South Hadley."
Plate 1 of Hitchcock's Ichnology of
Massachusetts, 1858.

An event in Greenfield marks the real beginning of Connecticut
Valley ichnology (study of stone prints).  In 1835, as sidewalks
were being paved with flat sandy-shale from a Turners Falls quarry,
many townspeople noticed curious "turkey tracks" in the rock.  It was
James Deane, M.D., who "alone recognized in their mute teachings sub-
lime indications of an Almighty hand...(and) entered upon the investi-
gation of the whole subject.""  The 35-year-old doctor wrote to 43-year-
old Professor Edward Hitchcock of Amherst College about the discovery.
Hitchcock replied that the features were probably not due to "organic
agencies" but Deane should acquire the specimens as he would visit

Greenfield in a month or two. Unable to contain his enthusiasm, Deane sent some plaster casts of the prints to Hitchcock who journeyed the 20 miles to Greenfield "a few days after."

> "No facts in my life are more vividly impressed upon my memory than those relating to the footmarks. I remember when I received Dr. Deane's first letter, that I feared it would turn out as I had known in many similar cases where tracks had been described to me, to be something quite different. But as soon as I saw the specimens, I perceived the phenomena worthy of careful research."[12]

Thus began almost 30 years of painstaking, detailed work, resulting in international fame and a unique contribution to science. In numerous journal articles and two books, Hitchcock described 154 species of animals based on the shale impressions, all carefully measured and sketched (Fig. 33). His collection of over 10,000 prints is preserved at Amherst College's Pratt Museum, and the now-abandoned quarry that produced a majority of the specimens can be visited at Barton Cove Nature Area, Route 2, Gill, Massachusetts.

As Hitchcock's fame grew, Greenfield's Dr. Deane felt slighted and vied for the honor of being the first to scientifically investigate the bird tracks. A stonemason, Dexter Marsh, wrote to claim the honor of discovering "the first specimen of fossil footprints of birds ever brought into public notice in this country," a claim also made by a Mr. Wilson.[13] Another version has Mr. W. W. Draper showing Mr. Wilson who showed Dexter Marsh who informed Dr. Deane.[14] In any case, Deane did investigate the tracks, publishing several journal articles and a book, but his first publication was not until 1843, seven years after Hitchcock's first paper. Deane was a great help in searching for new specimens and Hitchcock acknowledged Deane's assistance in his publications. He named a footprint species for Deane, and "secured for him, from the Trustees of Amherst College in 1838, the honorary degree of Master of Arts."[15] It seems clear, as history records, that Edward Hitchcock, clergyman, president of Amherst College, and state geologist should receive the accolades for his labors.

And what labors! Deciphering these geological hieroglyphics became Hitchcock's passion. In the beginning, he had to convince skeptical colleagues of the tracks' authenticity. Then there was the problem of analysis. What kinds of prehistoric creatures were these? After careful study of the foot structure of many animals, he concluded that our valley prints reveal a fauna dominated by large ostrich-like ground birds, accompanied by reptiles, amphibians, turtles, kangaroo-like "marsupialoids", worms, and insects. Uncertainty prevailed in many cases, especially in differentiating bird from reptile prints. The evidence of hollow bone structure seen in some of the rare Connecticut Valley fossils seemed to support an avian origin of the prints, as did the 1861 discovery in Solnhofen, Germany, of the famous fossil bird, Archeopteryx. Hitchcock believed that many of the tail prints could have been made by an Archeopteryx-type animal.

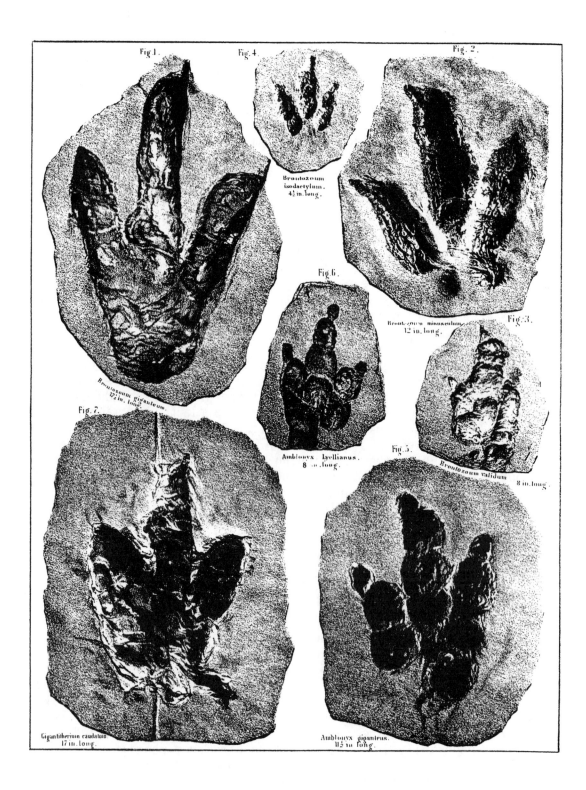

Figure 33 - Reproduction of Plate 57 from Hitchcock's
<u>Ichnology of Massachusetts</u> (1858).[12]

But where were the feather impressions?  Birds must have feathers and certainly some would have joined the fossil record along with the footprints, raindrops, mud cracks, etc.  Many of Hitchcock's "birds" showed impressions of front feet as well as the larger hind legs, and prominent tails.  Strange birds, indeed.  The uncertainties of ichnology forced Hitchcock to realize that his interpretations were "tossed on the sea of difficulty, and I cannot but hope that subsequent researchers will show that we have not cast anchor merely in quicksand."[16]

The anchor came to rest with the dinosaurs.  At the 1859 meeting of the American Association for the Advancement of Science in Springfield, Roswell Field, whose Gill farm included the Barton Cove footprint quarry, stated for the first time that dinosaurs were the makers of most of the prints.  The dinosaur evidence is based on the following.  Although hollow bones are found in birds, they are also characteristic of the birds' ancestors - thecodont reptiles.  Other bone characteristics also favor the reptiles.  The animals walked on hind legs rather than on all four, and had tails large enough to counterbalance their erect upper torso.  Finally, the earliest bird, Archeopteryx, dates from the Late Jurassic, 30 million years after our Early Jurassic Connecticut Valley prints.

Hitchcock was close.  Many of the prints certainly look like "turkey tracks."  I do not think that he would be upset by our revised view of Mesozoic fauna, but would state even more emphatically:

"What a wonderful menagerie!  Who would believe that
such a register lay buried in the strata?  To open the
leaves, to unroll the papyrus, has been an intensely interesting though difficult work, having all the excitement and marvelous developments of a romance.  And yet
the volume is only partly read.  Many a new page I fancy
will yet be opened..."[17]

Every split of a sedimentary rock exposes a never-before-seen page in the ancient history of our valley, perhaps revealing secrets of former inhabitants or their environment.  In 1966, excavation for a state building came to a halt when bulldozer operator Edward McCarthy noticed footprints in a slab of rock.  Their significance was verified, and Connecticut Governor John Dempsey preserved the site as Dinosaur State Park, just south of Hartford.

"The Rocky Hill site is remarkable in that it is perhaps the largest (more than 35,000 square feet) known
exposure with abundant fossil footprints preserved on
a single bedding plane (Fig. 34).  There are other
impressive footprint sites (Arizona, Texas, Basuto-
land), but all are in remote or wilderness regions
and are quite impractical to preserve.  To date,
more than 1,000 footprints have been studied and
identified in less than one-fourth of the area presently exposed at Rocky Hill.  Aside from the impressive spectacle of so many footprints and such a large
expanse, this site contains an unusual record of a

'single moment' in...time.  It provides documentation
of an ancient community of dinosaurs and related reptiles as living creatures approximately 200 million
years ago.  This record is preserved on a large expanse
of a single bedding surface - a bedding surface that
could well represent an interval of less than 24 hours
duration.  Rocky Hill can provide us with new information on animal associations, habits, and movement that
cannot be obtained from other...sites."[18]

As an example, a discovery by Dr. Walter P. Coombs, Jr., of Western
New England College:

"...sheds light on the swimming ability of carnivorous
dinosaurs.  It consists of eight successive footprints
[probably Eubrontes] averaging just over one meter between steps.  The step with the right foot forward is
consistently about 20 centimeters longer than the step
with the left foot, which suggests to Coombs that the
swimming movements had a kind of galloping rhythm.
Further, some of the prints show exceptionally clear
claw marks...and yet give no indication that the
animal was putting any weight on its feet.  According to Coomb's interpretation, the animal was swimming in shallow water, kicking the bottom with the
tips of its toes.  Moreover, the track sequence ends
abruptly, indicating that the swimming motion inter-
mittantly lifted the animal clear of the bottom.
Coombs concludes that the traditional image of the
frustrated carnivore standing at the water's edge
is in need of revision."[19]

Besides swimming, Eubrontes may also have hunted in groups, an
advanced social behavior.  Dr. John Ostrom of Yale tracked 19 pairs
of Eubrontes prints all heading westward across a sandstone layer near
the Connecticut River in Holyoke.[20]  Were they pursuing prey, mates, or
the sunset?  If only that bedding plane were larger!

When Bill Gingras started splitting and removing shale to make
room for a deck behind his small Granby, Massachusetts, home in 1968,
little did he realize how much that event would change his life.  Those
shale layers revealed the footsteps of the biggest animals ever recorded
in the Connecticut Valley.  In 1973, prints over three feet long were
uncovered (Fig. 35), representing a 50-foot-long carnivorous dinosaur
similar in size to Tyrannosaurus!  For comparison, Hitchcock's largest
print was only 1 1/2 feet long.  Because no bones are associated with
the prints, their biological heritage is unclear, but they, like Eubrontes, are probably ancestors to the world's greatest tyrant, Tyrannosaurus of Late Mesozoic times.  These and other specimens can be seen
at the Gingras' Granby Dinosaur Museum, purchased recently by the Common-
wealth of Massachusetts and being renovated.

Figure 34 - Dinosaur prints at Dinosaur State Park, Rocky Hill, Ct.
Crosses at 10-foot intervals. Photo courtesy Connecti-
cut State Geology and Natural History Survey, and W. H.
Freeman Company

Figure 35 - Large carnosaur print from the Granby Dinosaur Museum
Quarry on display at the Museum. Ruler is 12 inches.
Photo by the author.

Besides the large dinosaurs, many other reptiles and their rela-
tives inhabited our valley.  Table 2 lists and describes the more prominent members of our upper Triassic-lower Jurassic community.  See
Appendix III for drawings of the reptiles.

TABLE 2

### MESOZOIC REPTILES OF THE CONNECTICUT VALLEY

| NAME | DIET (Carnivore, Herbivore) | BODY LENGTH (in feet) | DESCRIPTION | BIOLOGICAL GROUPING |
|---|---|---|---|---|
| ANCHISAURUS | H, mainly | 6-9 | Four-toed, slender footed, bipedal )  Fossil bones from several localities, especially, Manchester, CT | )Prosauropod. )Descendants include )the giant, long- )necked Brontosaurus )and Diplodocus |
| AMMOSAURUS | H | 3-10 | Broad-footed, bipedal ) | |
| COELOPHYSIS (former name: Podokesaurus) | C | 3-10 | Light, active animal, known from 2 partial skeletons found in valley plus many from western U.S. and other parts of world.  Ate insects, smaller reptiles, and, perhaps, fish. The 3-toed tracks are named "Grallator" and "Anchisauripus". | Coelurosaur. Descendant:  Ostrich dinosaur, Ornithomimus |
| Eubrontes*   ) Gigantipus*  ) | C | about 10 to approx. 50 or more (Gigantipus) | Large, bipedal, 3-toed Carnosaurs, tracks range from about 8 inches to 3  feet.  No bone fossils. | Carnosaurs. Descendant: Tyrannosaurus |
| ANOMOEPUS*  ) SAUROPUS*   ) | H | ? | Four-footed, 3 toes on hind foot, 5 toes on front, hind prints about 16 inches, front print about 2 1/2 inches; no bone remains | ORNITHOPOD (?) |
| OTOZOUM* | ? | ? | Four-footed, 4 toes on hind feet, five on front, 2-6 inch prints probably made by small thecodont reptiles. | Thecodont |
| BATRACHOPUS* | ? | Less than 1 | Four-footed, 4-toed, 1-2 inch prints, probably made by Stegomosuchus, a primitive crocodile. | Crocodile (?) |
| STEGOMUS       ) STEGOMOSUCHUS ) | C | about 1/2 | Heavily armored, 4-footed.  Perhaps primtive crocodiles.  Two partial skeletons:  Longmeadow, MA, and Fairhaven, CT. | Crocodile (?) |
| BELODON | C | May reach 20 | Four-footed crocodile-like animal.  Fossil shoulder blade from Simsbury, CT. | Phytosaur |
| HYPSOGNATHUS | H | About 1 | Four-footed, lizard-like animal bones from Meriden, CT. | Procolophonid Reptile |

*These names refer to tracks whose "owners" are either unknown or uncertain.  Many other tracks have been named
 (see Hitchcock, 1858) and are probably due to unknown small reptiles and, perhaps, amphibians.

Data compiled from Colbert, 1970; Ostrom, 1968; McDonald, 1982, and other sources

## FISH

"Fossil fishing" along the bed of the Connecticut River is a favor-
ite pastime for paleontologists and amateurs alike.  Look for dark shales
of the oxygen-poor former lake bottom, split carefully along the layers
and you may be rewarded with coal black impressions of fish scales, fins,
or the supreme catch -- a whole specimen over two feet long!

The stagnant condition of the lake floor prevented decomposition
of the organic remains, and also limited the action of predators, so the

fish are frequently whole and beautifully preserved (Fig. 36). If only a dinosaur, a big carnosaur, could have swum or floated to the middle of a valley lake, died, and sunk to be preserved in that embalming black blanket. What a find that would be!

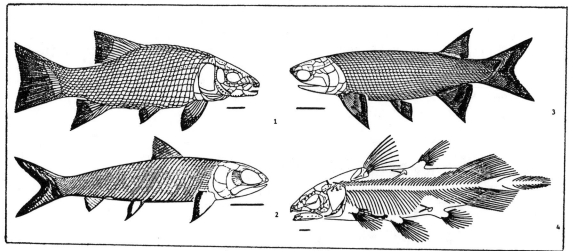

Figure 36 - Fossil fish from the Connecticut Valley. (1) A generalized semionotid; (2) Ptycholepis marshi; (3) Redfieldius gracilis; (4) Diplurus newarki. Bar equals one inch. (Compiled from several sources by McDonald, 1982).[21]

Lakes were common in early Jurassic times as the climate became wetter and lava started to cover our valley, blocking stream channels. Black shales and their entombed fish are lacking in the upper Triassic rocks below the lavas but are abundant on the east side of our valley where the younger Jurassic strata lie on top of the lavas (see Fig. 5).

Four genera of fish have been described ranging from 1/2 to 2 1/2 feet in length. Semionotus, our most common fish fossil, reached lengths up to 16 inches. It was a predator with peg-like teeth, able to suck in prey as well as nibble vegetation. The rarely found Ptycholepis, also found in European marine strata, is thought to have swum to our ancient lakes from the sea. Even rarer is our largest fish predator, a 2 1/2 foot coelacanth, Diplurus.

Besides their beautiful skeletons, fish coprolites (fossil feces) are commonly found.

"They vary in shape from round or ovoid to cigar shaped, and range in length from a few millimeters to greater than 15 cm. Most are structureless masses of black, carbonaceous material but several, particularly from the East Berlin Formation, contain disassociated fish scales and bones."[21]

Several fish skeletons have been found with coprolites still inside.

# INVERTEBRATES

Organic evidence is rare, but invertebrates must have been abundant based on their numerous trails and burrows, and the fact that they
would have been at the base of the food chain.  Some lake inhabitants so
far discovered include small (2 inch long) mussels and tiny zooplankton
(ostracods and "clam shrimp").  Shale and sandstone record evidence of
worm and crayfish burrows and trails of many creatures including insects (adult and larval), crustaceans, worms, and snails.  Dragonfly
larvae, known as Mormolucoides, left abundant remains in the valley
mud.  The half-inch long fossils have 13 segments.  Figure 37 illustrates our valley's invertebrate record.

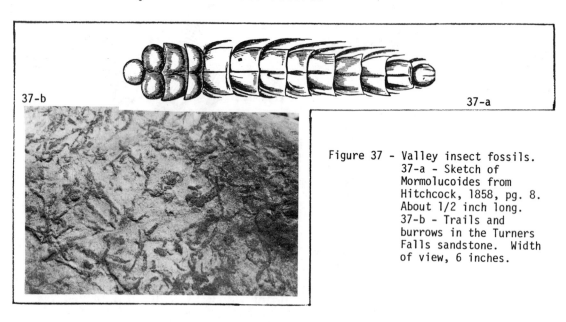

37-b                                                                 37-a

Figure 37 - Valley insect fossils.
37-a - Sketch of
Mormolucoides from
Hitchcock, 1858, pg. 8.
About 1/2 inch long.
37-b - Trails and
burrows in the Turners
Falls sandstone.  Width
of view, 6 inches.

# PLANTS

Dinosaurs never stepped on grass.  It would be Miocene times,
150 million years after the Connecticut Valley dinoprints, before
grasses evolved with their soil-holding roots.  Grasses would have
greatly diminished our dinoprints.  Sod does not preserve tracks as
precisely as mud and also reduces hillside erosion and floods which
are necessary ingredients to cover and preserve the prints.

Since the base of almost all ecosystems rests with plant productivity, plants must have been numerous to support our reptile populations.  Ferns, horsetails, and cycads, common tropical plants, inhabited moist stream and lake shore environments, and on the drier
alluvial fans and adjacent mountains, impressive spruce-like conifers
reached 180 foot heights (see Fig. 20).

Some of the southern Mesozoic fault valleys (see Fig. 19) have extensive coal beds, but the Connecticut Valley was drier and preserved a rather sparse vegetation record for the same reason the dinobones were lost: oxidation and decay. Occasional carbonized stems, trunks, leaves, needles, and cones are found, but usually their organic forms rotted. Sometimes sand seeped into the decayed spaces, preserving a rough outline of the stem or branch. Roots occasionally became encased with calcium to form root cast concretions. Lava preserved at least one valley plant. In 1898, B. K. Emmerson, eminent geologist and successor to Hitchcock at Amherst, reported a Deerfield lava sample (collected by Hitchcock) "...where a branch was enclosed in the liquid lava, burned, and the cavity immediately filled with lava from above."[22]

One of the most spectacular plant discoveries is fossil pollen and spores, preserved in our Mesozoic lake sediments. After the shale is dissolved in acid, these resistant 180-million-year-old microscopic reproductive structures can be analyzed. Twenty-seven genera have been identified revealing conifers as the major constituent and a climate dominated by wet and dry seasons with between four and twenty inches of annual rainfall.

Correlation of the plant species, supported by evidence from fossil fish, has revealed that our valley is younger than we had believed it to be. Valley events and fossils were formerly thought to represent Triassic times, but now, only the lower formations (those below the lava flows) are classed as Late Triassic; the lavas and later formations are Early to Mid Jurassic (Fig. 38).[23]

## A JURASSIC PARADISE ?

If, by time machine, we are ever able to visit our Mesozoic valley, we would find a spectacularly beautiful environment (see Fig. 28), much like the scenic valleys nestled along the eastern fringe of California's Sierra Nevada Mountains. Temperatures would be mild year-around since our latitude was 10° north of the equator (similar to Central America). High humidity discomfort during the several months of the rainy season would be balanced by excellent dry season weather.

The best home sites would be in the bedrock hills along the east rim of our valley where real estate agents would extol excellent valley views, earthquake resistance (being on bedrock), and safety from roving carnosaurs (hopefully, they would stay on the flatlands and chase reptilian herbivores). Just a short jaunt along mountain streams flowing over alluvial fans would bring us to lakes with both recreational and irrigational potential. Farming would be excellent in the lake and floodplain soils along the margins of the rocky alluvial fans. During droughts, water could be drawn from valley lakes or wells dug in the water-rich alluvial fan gravels. Natural hot tubs and saunas could be enjoyed as hot springs seeped upward along the border faults. The travel possibilities were truly unique -- overland connections to all Pangaea. But hurry, this offer lasts for only a few more million years!

44

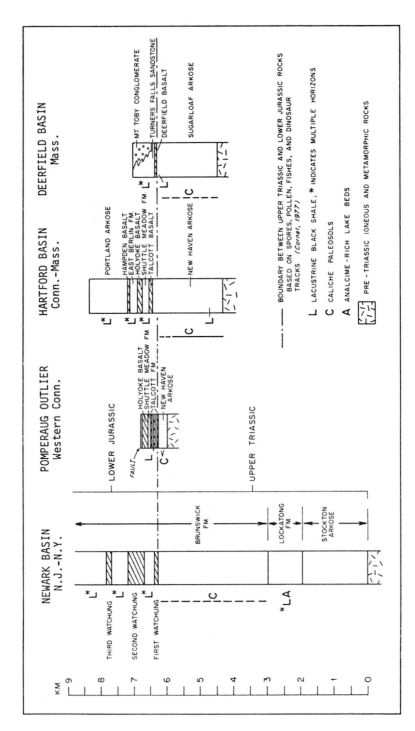

Figure 38 - Stratigraphy of Upper Triassic and Lower Jurassic rocks in the Newark, Hartford, and Deerfield Basins, and in the Pomperaug Outlier. The thickness for each formation is the maximum value so that at any one locality, the total section is not as thick as shown on the diagram. (From Hubert, et al, 1978).[1]

Some serious environmental hazards would have to be faced.  The
Eastern Border Fault would be quite a threat, but it is likely that a
truly devastating quake would occur only every other century.  Of
course, dinosaurs would present problems.  Besides avoiding falling
prey to the carnosaurs, herbivores would have to be kept out of the
fields.  Since there were many times more herbivores than carnivores,
the former might have caused more havoc.  The great carnosaurs were
probably rare visitors to the valley, based on the paucity of their prints.

## CRETACEOUS ENDINGS : the MESOZOIC , the VALLEY,  and the DINOSAURS

By Cretaceous times, the ancestral Connecticut Valley had vanished,
destroyed by streams that eroded eastern hills, filling the valley to its
brim (Fig. 39).  The Eastern Border Fault, creator of the valley, became
inactive as North America and Europe/Africa finally parted company.  The
ultimate erosional stage was now reached -- the peneplane, a gently slop-
ing landscape graded to the sea level of the "new" Atlantic Ocean.  A
few higher places, being harder to erode, remained above the peneplain
and are known as "monadnocks" after the type example, Mt. Monadnock of
southern New Hampshire.

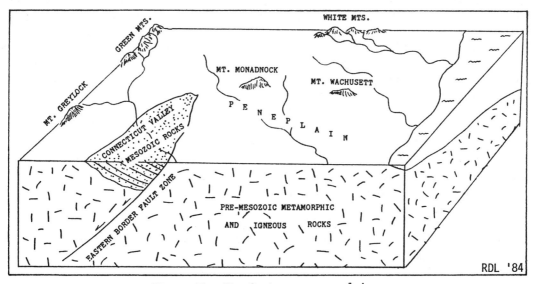

Figure 39 - The Cretaceous peneplain.

Dinosaurs loved this environment.  There were extensive oceanfront
pastures for foraging and no mountain passes to negotiate.  The Cretaceous
is the time of spectacular dinosaurs.  Vegetarians such as descendants
of the 30 ton, long-necked, long-tailed Brontosaurus, the three-horned
Triceratops, and the curious "duck-billed" dinosaurs were probably
tramping across our peneplain, chased by giant carnosaurs such as Tyrannosaurus.  But, alas, we have no record of these inhabitants since
the thin soils and sediments of the peneplain, where their remains
might have been preserved, have been lost to erosion.  However, a few
fossils are preserved in Late Cretaceous coastal sediments found along

the Atlantic Coastal Plain. From New Jersey come many bones of the duck-billed <u>Hadrosaurs</u>, including the world's first dinosaur bone found in 1787. [24]

Sixty-five million years ago, as we entered our most recent era, the Cenozoic, fifty percent of all plant and animal genera became extinct! Gone are all the dinosaurs after over 150 million years of ruling land, sea, and air. The earth was left to the course of mammalian evolution.

Was fifty percent of Cretaceous life exterminated by a large meteorite impact? It is frightening to think that massive extraterrestrial catastrophes are responsible for great biological changes, as opposed to more gradual "natural" variations in our Earth environment, such as continental drift and climate change.

Support for extraterrestrial catastrophism comes from several lines of evidence. High concentrations of iridium and osmium, elements more common in meteorites than earth rock, are found in clay layers deposited during the Mesozoic-Cenozoic transition. A large meteorite impact would create massive environmental effects, such as darkness for months and atmospheric pollution. A fatal blow was dealt to dinosaurs and many other organisms, but plants, because of the abundance of resistant, leaf-dropping species and seeds to spawn new generations, and mammals, being small burrowing creatures, were much less affected by the impact.

Recently, a 30-million-year cycle of extinctions has been discovered.[25] No earthly or astronomic process is known to explain this, but several scenarios have us being bombarded with killer comets and meteorites. As our solar system passes through denser bands of the Milky Way, gravitation effects could redirect comets into the Earth's path. A similar gravitational tug could be provided by a sister star to our sun. None has so far been discovered, but most stars have rotating companions. Since earthly craters also seem to display a 30 million year impact cycle, credence is added to some sort of astronomic process whose next arrivals are due in about 15 million years.

It is comforting to know that we could deflect a meteorite on a collision course with Earth by exploding missiles on or near the object. Space stations would be necessary to identify and track the invader, and missile guidance systems would have to be developed.

> "For those among us who favor a return to a simpler
> way of life, less dependent on advanced technologies, as
> a route to human survival, there is a lesson in all this.
> The event which could wreak havoc on a global scale more
> certainly than any other can be averted, but only if we
> devote the most advanced of our technologies to the pro-
> blem. If the risk is real -- and it is -- human survival
> and very possibly the survival of most life on this planet
> can be assured only with the aid of high technology. It
> is not that life itself might be extinguished on the
> planet, but the direction of its future development might
> be changed. Our ancestors may have benefited from the

last such change, but would we benefit now?  Can we be
sure there is not some small, insignificant group of
animals whose further development awaits our departure?
Next time will we fill the role of the dinosaurs?" [26]


Hopefully, we can survive the next 15 million years' geopolitics,
ice ages, and other climate variations to prepare for the coming collisions.

Proposed origin of valley dinoprints.

# PART FOUR                    the Cenozoic

# REBIRTH of the VALLEY

## UPLIFTING The PENEPLAIN:   The Connecticut River Begins

It was easy to reach the ocean in Late Cretaceous-Early Cenozoic times. Sluggish meandering streams made their way across the peneplain erosion surface bringing sand to the beach zone at Waterbury and Middletown, or perhaps further inland. Although the record of the ocean's foray into New England has been erased by erosion, we find abundant evidence of shell-rich beach and near-shore sediment in the Atlantic Coastal Plain from New York to Florida. Cretaceous coastal plain sediments are under the glacial deposits of Cape Cod and Georges Bank, where they may contain oil and natural gas.

As great new mountains rose in the Rockies, the aged eastern peneplain shifted restlessly and warped upward (without folding or faulting) several thousand feet in the Connecticut Valley area. We know that most of the uplift occurred in Late Miocene times, about 10 million years ago, since coarse sands and gravels of active streams left their mark in the coastal plain record. The arching was caused by movements in the mantle, probably related to continental drift and the continued growth of the Atlantic.

Uplift rejuvenates streams. The sluggish "old" meandering rivers now had steeper slopes and faster flow, and this erosive potential was put to work engraving V-shaped canyons into the rising peneplain. "Nothing under the heaven is softer or more yielding than water; but when it attacks things hard and resistant, there is not one of them that can prevail," said a Chinese scholar more than 2,000 years ago.' Water will do its greatest erosional work in the easiest places - soft rocks. Our red rock "inlay" is a weak link in the geologic mosaic of southern New England, and from this weakness, the Connecticut Valley was born.

Pirate streams, which flowed southerly over our weak sedimentary rocks, changed the drainage pattern of southern New England. Since they could erode faster than the others, they became deeper and steeper and captured adjacent drainage areas (Fig. 40). The Deerfield, Westfield, and Farmington rivers were united by river pirates to become the great Connecticut River, an apt name, for our river connected the Deerfield and Hartford Basins for the first time. With the Connecticut being the quickest and steepest route to the sea, pirates extended their drainage empire into Vermont and New Hampshire, beyond the limits of our sedimentary rocks, following linear zones of weak metamorphic rock and faults left by Appalachian mountain building. And so, by capturing others, New England's mightiest river was created.

For 200 miles, from St. Johnsbury, Vermont, to Middletown, Connecticut, the river flowed southward, following geologic trends, then abruptly turned southeastward for its final dash to the sea. Why would the Connecticut leave the easily-eroded red rock valley for a path

through the resistant metamorphic rocks of the Eastern Highlands?  A
look at the geologic map (Fig. 2) gives one clue:  lava.  The resistant basalt lavas near Middletown are concentrated at the east side of
the valley, forcing the Connecticut out of the soft sedimentary rocks
and onto the hard metamorphics.  Another clue is the path of the original Farmington River (see Fig. 40-a).  As the rivers deepened their
valleys in response to uplift of the peneplain, the Farmington became
the major drainage route to the sea.  The pirates were, in effect,
adding to the Farmington River system.  Perhaps we should change the
Connecticut's name.

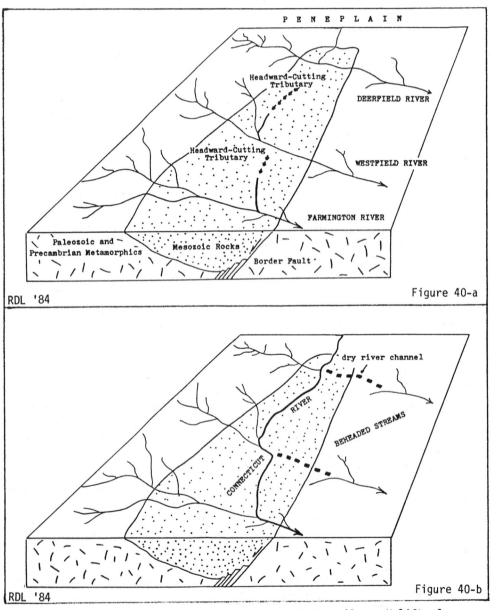

Figure 40 - Development of the Connecticut River:  40-a - Uplift of
            peneplain allows "pirate" tributaries to actively extend
            their valley (headward-cutting); 40-b - By intersecting
            and diverting adjacent streams, the Connecticut is created.

# TOPOGRAPHY and TOMBSTONES

The New England landscape was thought to record three or four periods of uplift and erosion.  As the initial peneplain uplifted, rivers etched their valley systems into the raised peneplain, creating a river erosion level below the upland remnants of the first (Fig. 41).  Renewed uplift started the streams on their erosional cycle again, creating a third level below the remnants of the previous two, and so on.  However, it seems that the various erosional levels, rather than representing separate uplift-erosion cycles, are due to variations in rock resistance.  As any graveyard stroll will verify, all rocks are not created equal.  Some, like granite, can weather several hundred years without the slightest hint of deterioration.  Others, such as marble and brownstone, lose their engraved details in a geological instant.  (Be sure to consider this when planning your geological future.)

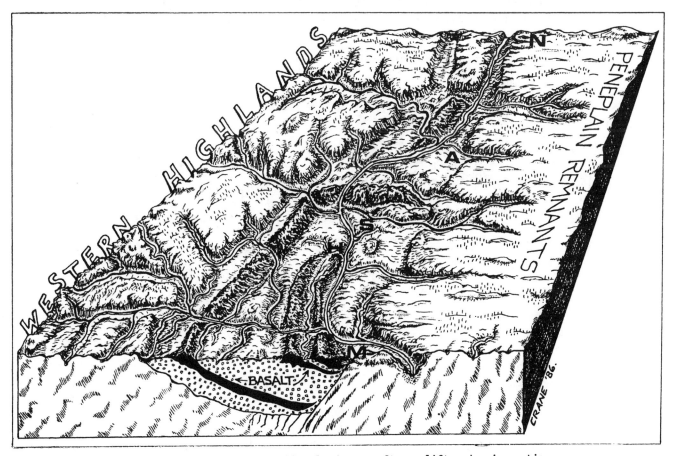

Figure 41 - Mid-Cenozoic valley landscape after uplift and rejuvenation of streams.  N = Northfield; A = Amherst; S - Springfield; H = Hartford; M - Middletown.

Uplift of the original Late Mesozoic peneplain started the erosional processes in motion.  As they etched the bedrock mosaic, resistant rocks remained higher than the weaker rocks.  A cross section just south of the

Massachusetts-Connecticut border (Fig. 42) reveals these etched rela-
tionships.   If erosion continues at present rates, we can expect a new
New England peneplain in about 30-40 million years,  unless the restless
mantle has other plans.

How do rivers cut through ridges?  The Connecticut Valley has some
striking "water gaps".  The Connecticut cuts through the Holyoke Range,
the Deerfield slices the Pocumtuck Range, the Westfield dissects Provin
and East Mountain, and the Farmington has two channels through the Talcott basalt:  at Tariffville and at an abandoned gorge at Cooks Gap west
of New Britain.  As uplift of the peneplain began, the rivers that
flowed across resistant rock areas eroded through them while the sur-
roundings were lowered (see Fig. 41).

Our valley rivers and their water gaps would be even more impressive if we could see the bedrock river beds.  Initiated by the Late

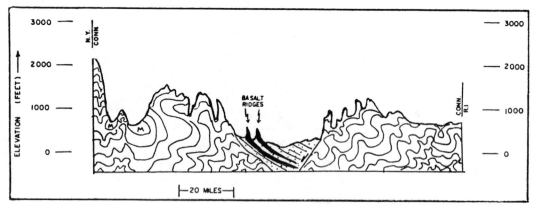

Figure 42-a - Cross section of northern Connecticut at 42° north latitude.[2]
The subsurface geology is sketched diagrammatically.
M = Marble; Dots = Connecticut Valley.

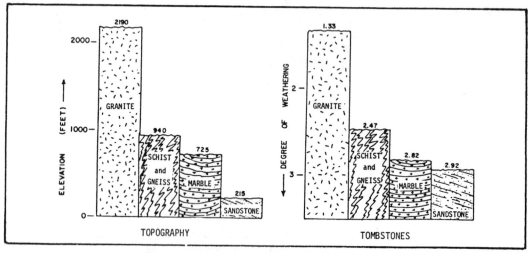

Figure 42-b - Comparison of topographic elevations and rates of
tombstone weathering (After Rahn, 1971).[2]

Miocene uplift, erosion created deep canyons reaching several hundred feet below present sea level! Deposition of glacial-age and recent sediments has hidden these gorges, not only from sight, but also from the present-day streams (Fig. 43). The deep valleys are actively sought after by hydrologists for their potential stores of ground water in coarse-grained channel deposits and are sometimes encountered during construction. A 300-foot-deep gorge (200 feet below present sea level) was found at the sites of the Sunderland and Northampton bridges over the Connecticut, and many other deep-buried valleys have been discovered throughout New England.

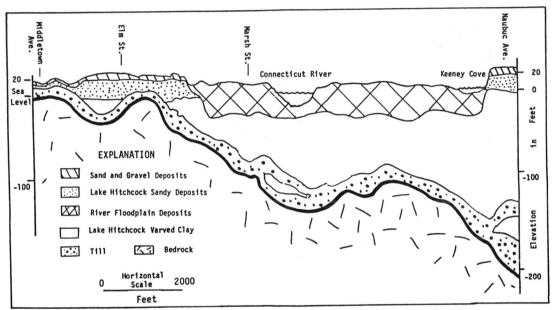

Figure 43 - Contrast between the earth's surface and bedrock, Hartford South quadrangle, Connecticut (Modified from R.E. Deane, 1967)[3]

If the border fault had not tiled our valley rocks, erosion would have created a very different landscape. Mesas and buttes would abound (Fig. 44), certainly to be inhabited by ancient (and perhaps modern) cliff-

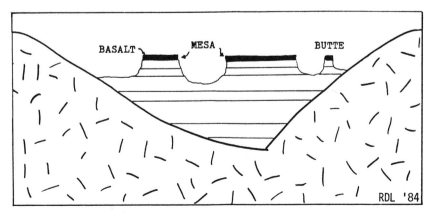

Figure 44 - Hypothetical valley landforms developed on flat-lying rock.

dwellers. As tilted rocks eroded, the resistant basalts emerged with characteristic cliff and dip-slope profiles. When standing on scenic ridge-top lookouts, many people envision great quakes pushing the ridges upward above the lowlands, but the origin of these spectacular cliffs is really quite boring: millions of years of erosion (Fig. 45). Because the valley layers dip to the east, cliffs develop facing west. However, a series of faults in the northeastern Holyoke Range bends the cliff to face north, overlooking Amherst (see Fig. 27).

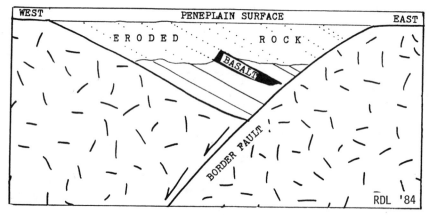

Figure 45 - Valley landscape developed due to erosion of tilted layers.

# THE ICE AGE

"Twenty thousand years ago, the landscape of North America
was so different that time travelers from the present would
find it very difficult to orient themselves.  The South-
western United States, rather than being a desert, was a
land of large freshwater lakes and lush vegetation.  In
place of the present vast open prairie of the Great Plains
there was a dense forest dominated by spruce and birch
trees and populated by browsing mammoths, musk ox, and
elk.  Even the shape of the continent was different, because a lower sea level resulted in the exposure of
thousands of square kilometers of additional land.  The
most profound differences from the present would be
found in the northern part of the continent.  There,
bordered by a belt of frozen tundra, was an ice sheet
that covered more than a third of North America.  The
entire earth, in fact, was still in the grip of a Great
Ice Age."[4]

The Wisconsinan Ice Sheet, named after that state's abundant glacial
deposits, is the most recent of over 20 glacial advances during the last
2 1/3 million years.  Although many of these did not reach as far south
as the Connecticut Valley, the two-mile-thick Wisconsinan ice effectively
blanketed New England (Fig. 46).  Even Mt. Washington's 6,300-foot summit
is capped by erratic boulders, mementos of victorious ice over vanquished

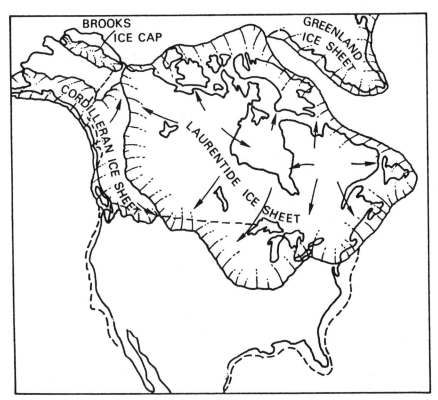

Figure 46 - Approximate maximum extent of major ice sheets in
North America during the Great Ice Age.  Ice caps
and glaciers in the mountains of the Western United States are not shown.  Dashed line is approximate coastline during full-glacial development
(From Matsch, 1976).[5]

56

mountain.  Ice erosion robbed rich, thick soil and surface rock from inland areas, but dumped its plunder to create the magnificent coastal
landscapes of Long Island, Cape Cod, Martha's Vineyard, and Nantucket,
as well as coating New England hills with an average of 10 feet of bouldery "till", source of picturesque stone walls.

Early 18th Century beliefs interpreted till and other glacial features as due to the swirling currents of Noah's flood, a view unsupported
by both field evidence and hydrologic theory.  In a sense, a great flood
did occur, but the water was solid (and the ark was an iceboat?).

The origin and characteristics of commonly encountered glacial landforms of New England are listed in Figure 47.

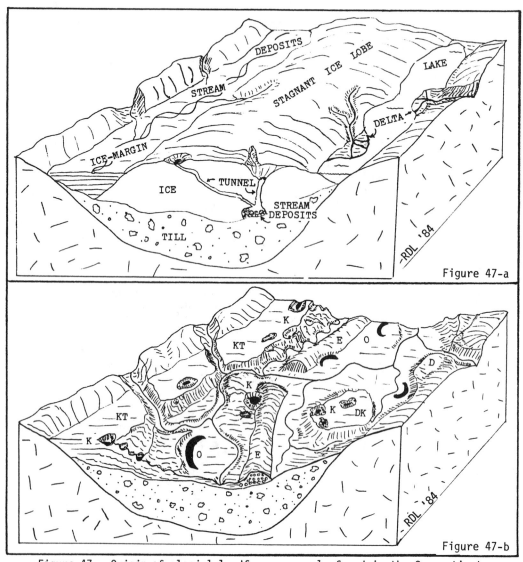

Figure 47 - Origin of glacial landforms commonly found in the Connecticut
Valley region.
Figure 47-a and 47-b - Before and after views of landforms
created in stagnant ice zones.  K = Kettle Hole (caused by
collapse as adjacent or underlying ice melts); KT = Kame
Terrace; O = Oxbow Lake (former stream channel; note curving shape and floodplain location as compared to kettles);
E = Esker (former stream deposit in ice); DK = Delta Kame
(delta built in contact with ice); D = Delta ("normal"
stream deposit, not in contact with ice).

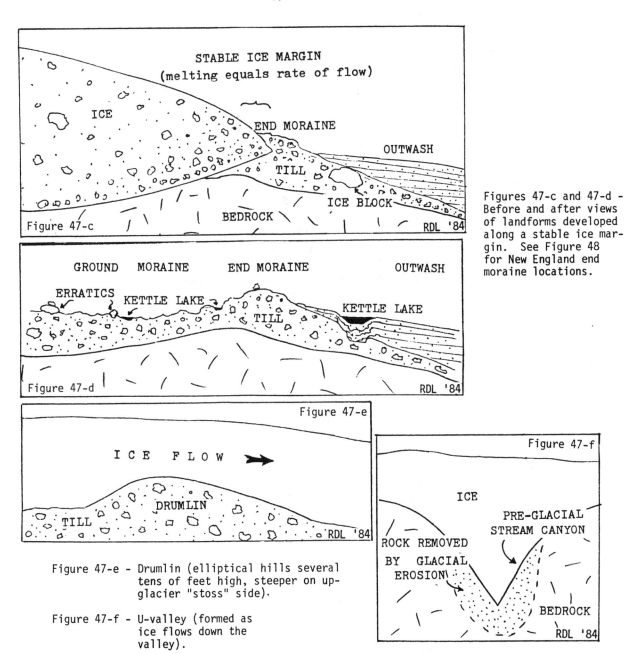

STABLE ICE MARGIN
(melting equals rate of flow)

ICE

END MORAINE

OUTWASH

TILL

ICE BLOCK

BEDROCK

Figure 47-c

RDL '84

GROUND MORAINE   END MORAINE        OUTWASH

ERRATICS   KETTLE LAKE

KETTLE LAKE

TILL

Figure 47-d

RDL '84

Figures 47-c and 47-d -
Before and after views
of landforms developed
along a stable ice mar-
gin. See Figure 48
for New England end
moraine locations.

Figure 47-e

I C E   F L O W

DRUMLIN

TILL

RDL '84

Figure 47-e - Drumlin (elliptical hills several
tens of feet high, steeper on up-
glacier "stoss" side).

Figure 47-f - U-valley (formed as
ice flows down the
valley).

Figure 47-f

ICE

PRE-GLACIAL
STREAM CANYON

ROCK REMOVED
BY GLACIAL
EROSION

BEDROCK

RDL '84

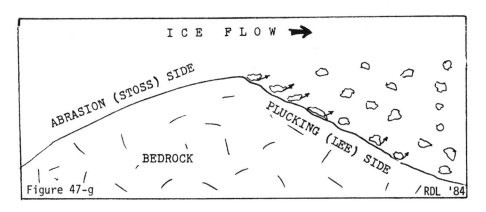

I C E   F L O W

ABRASION (STOSS) SIDE

PLUCKING (LEE) SIDE

BEDROCK

Figure 47-g

RDL '84

Figure 47-g - Roche Moutonnee (abrasion and plucking of bedrock;
forms can vary from mountain-top to table-top sizes).

The flat Midwest has many well-formed end moraines, a bit of topographic excitement left by the retreating ice. By contrast, New England has very few moraines (Fig. 48). Building a moraine requires active ice, the "dirt machine," to supply the ice front. The friction of New England's hilly topography, combined with thinning of the glacier by melting, resulted in a stagnant fringe of ice over much of New England. The margin of our once-active glacier became a gigantic, passive ice cube, creating sequences of landforms somewhat different from the Midwest. Like frigid Swiss cheese, the stagnant ice became riddled with holes and tunnels as the meltwater transit system hauled glacial debris to the outwash plain at the ice margin. Eskers, formed by stream deposits in the ice, reveal their unique, sinuous ridge-forms as the ice melts. All varieties of kames abound as meltwater deposited gravel in contact with the ice (see Fig. 47-a and 47-b). Kettles develop as buried ice blocks melt, forming ponds if the hole penetrates the water table.

Melting thinned the glacier and released the highlands from its icy grip, but tongues of stagnant ice clogged the upland valleys. Blocked drainage created lakes which lasted for a few months or years until the ice dams melted. Great floods occurred as the ice dams gave way, allowing the impounded water to flood down valley. These types of floods are a serious hazard in glacial regions today. Streams built deltas in the short-lived lakes and kame terraces along the ice margins, providing flat, gravelly land for the future development of "hilltowns".

The Connecticut Valley ice did not pass passively into meltwater oblivion. Being a thick lobe trapped in the confines of our valley walls, it remained active during retreat as surrounding areas thinned and stagnated. Scratched bedrock and deposits due to the active valley ice lobe have recently been documented, including locations where Lake Hitchcock clay (see next section) was "bulldozed" by advancing ice. At least 16 stillstands of the active ice front have been mapped in the vicinity of the Holyoke Range.[5] Two of these frontal positions with their associated landforms are illustrated in Figure 49.

Only 180 centuries ago, a mere yesterday of geological time, the ice began to retreat from its terminal regions of Long Island and Georges Bank. As the climate warmed, increased melting became greater than the gravity-induced flow of the ice. When melting exceeds the rate of ice movement, the ice front appears to move backward, or retreat. If the rate of flow and melting are approximately equal, the active ice front will remain at a stable position (stillstand) and, like a conveyor belt, dump a pile of till called end moraine.

From Long Island to Nantucket and along Cape Cod, end moraines and associated meltwater deposits (outwash) were important landscape formers (see Fig. 48). In fact, without these depositional artifacts of the ice, our southern New England coast would be deprived of its major recreational areas.

59

Figure 48 - Distribution of Wisconsinan moraines and ice-readvance
localities in New England.  B = Bridgeport readvance;
BBM = Buzzards Bay moraine; CM = Charlestown moraine;
C-MM = Cherryfield to Machias moraines; EB = East Bar-
net readvance; EM = Ellisville moraine; FPM = Fresh
Pond moraine; GQM = Great Quittacas Pond moraine; HHM =
Harbor Hill moraine; HM = Hardwick moraine; KM = Ken-
nebec moraines; KK = Kennebunk readvance; LM = Ledyard
moraine; MA = Manchester readvance; MI = Middletown
readvance (questionable); MT = Mount Tom readvance;
NM = Nantucket moraine; PJM = Point Judith moraine;
RM = Ronkonkoma moraine; SCM = South Coventry moraine;
SM = Sandwich moraine (From Koteff and Pessl, 1981).[7]

60

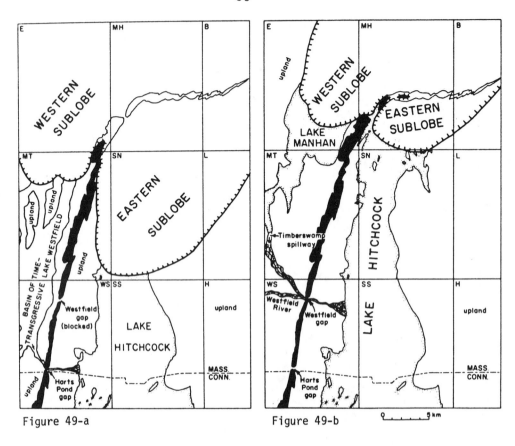

Figure 49-a

Figure 49-b

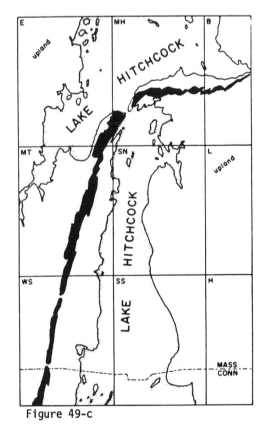

Figure 49-c

Figure 49 -

Paleogeography during
ice retreat in the
Holyoke Range (black).
(From Larsen and
Hartshorn, 1982).[6]

# LAKE HITCHCOCK

Approximately 14,000 years ago, a temporary lake developed along the front of the Connecticut Valley ice lobe in Rocky Hill. Streams deposited deltas that not only filled the lake but also created a barrier across the valley. This delta dam was the beginning of New England's largest glacial lake, Lake Hitchcock, which eventually extended along the Connecticut River Valley for 150 miles to Lyme, New Hampshire (Fig. 50).

Do delta deposits make a good dam? Absolutely not! They are permeable and easily eroded. Fortunately, as the lake water gradually rose and over-flowed the dam, the spillway happened to develop on bedrock; otherwise, the whole dam would have been rapidly cut through, ending Lake Hitchcock's brief existence. An initial spillway at Rocky Hill was abandoned for a lower, more stable outlet in New Britain, and although the gravelly delta dam has suffered much development, the spillway channels can still be recognized.

Lake Hitchcock would have been an impressive sight. Hemmed in by tundra-coated highlands, the lake gradually lengthened as a glacial cliff spawned icebergs to the whim of wind and currents. Melting bergs bombed their enclosed sediment on the lake floor, forming "dropstones" in the mud.

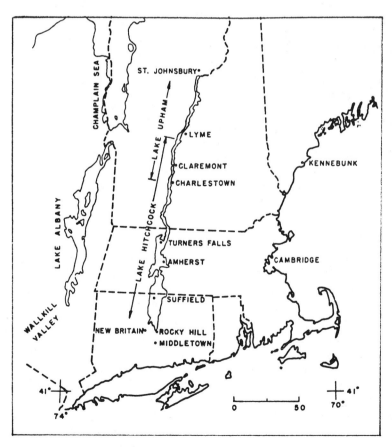

Figure 50 - Location map of Lake Hitchcock. Lake Upham formed after Hitchcock drained (From Ashley, 1972).

62

Swollen by glacial meltwater, streams brought prodigious amounts of sediment into Lake Hitchcock and rapidly built deltas (Fig. 51). Deltas give us our most important geologic resources: sand and gravel. It is easy to spot deltas. Look for flat-topped gravel pits. The working face of the pit will commonly display distinctive inclined layers, foreset beds, deposited along the steep frontal slope of the delta (Fig. 52). Flat-lying, coarser stream gravels form topset beds capping the foresets, and occasionally, the deeper, sandy-silty bottomset beds are revealed. The shoreline and prominent deltas of Lake Hitchcock are mapped on Figures 53 and 54.

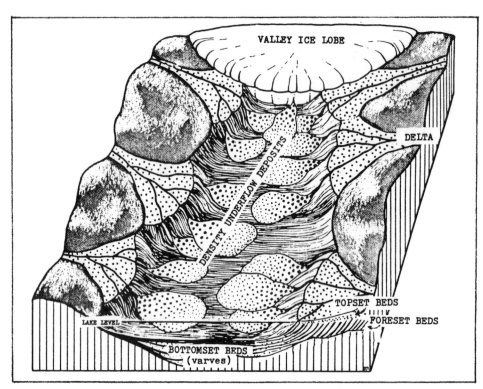

Figure 51 - Deposits of Lake Hitchcock (Modified from Ashley, 1972).[9]

North and northeast winds swept across the narrow lake, creating waves which eroded small cliffs and deposited sand and gravel beaches in protected lake-shore zones. Deltas and beaches are repositories for sand and gravel, but what about finer sediment -- mud? Glacial streams are notoriously dirty ("too thick to drink, too thin to walk on") with the "milk" or "rock flour" from ice abrasion. These fine sediments flowed in turbid "density underflows" along the lake bottom before settling (Fig. 51). During winter when stream flow was quiescent, clay became the predominant lake bottom deposit. Spring snowmelt and rainfall enabled streams to carry coarser sediment, such as fine sand and silt, into the lake bed. These yearly pairs of clay and silt or sand, called varves, can be seen in construction sites and stream banks across the lower valley elevations (Fig. 55) and commonly reach thicknesses of over 200 feet.

63

Figure 52 - Internal structure of a delta, Northfield, MA.
Flat topset beds overlie foresets (arrows).

How long Lake Hitchcock existed in the valley is a controversial
problem first investigated in the 1920s by Ernst Antevs.[10] He braved the
slippery mud of brickyard clay pits to count and measure varves and
pieced together the growth of the lake, year by year. Antevs recognized a total of 4,100 varves, equal to 4,100 years of history, but it
seems unlikely that the lake could have lasted that long. More recent
study of valley varves indicates that Antevs' count may be too high
since the variable sediment loads of Hitchcock's tributary streams com-
plicates varve thicknesses, making correlations and dating difficult.[9]
The lake is estimated to have begun about 13,700 years ago as the ice
retreated to Rocky Hill, and drainage is dated at 10,700 B.P. (Before
Present) based on two radiocarbon dates at a locality north of Hanover,
New Hampshire.[11] However, archeological evidence (see next section) suggests that draining occurred as early as 12,900 years ago. Until more
organic material is found and dated, the precise history of the rise and
fall of great Lake Hitchcock is enigmatic.

Congratulations are due the Rocky Hill dam for withstanding the forces
of erosion for several thousand years. Stream erosion finally breached
the dam, releasing lake waters to flood the lower Connecticut to the sea.
The demise of our 150-mile-long lake probably occurred in four flood pul-
ses, since delta-building streams had partitioned Lake Hitchcock into a
series of lakes: Lake Springfield (south and east of the Holyoke Range);
Lake Hadley (north of the Holyoke Range to Deerfield and Amherst); Lake
Montague (east of the Pocumtuck Range); and Lake Northfield (north of the
Millers River Delta to Lyme, New Hampshire). After the Rocky Hill dam
failed, these secondary obstructions were breached and sequentially released their water volumes.

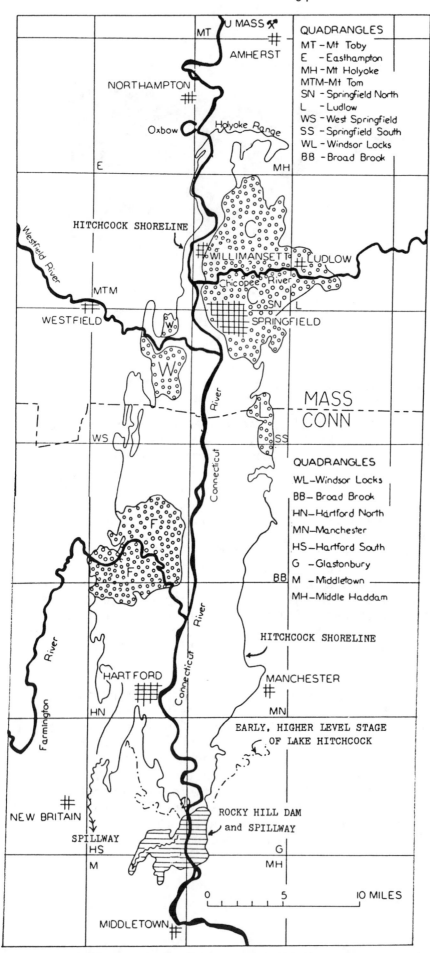

Figure 53 – Lake Hitchcock shoreline and major deltas south of the Holyoke Range. Delta labels: F = Farmington; W = Westfield; L = Longmeadow; C = Chicopee (From Hartshorn and Colton, 1967).[8]

65

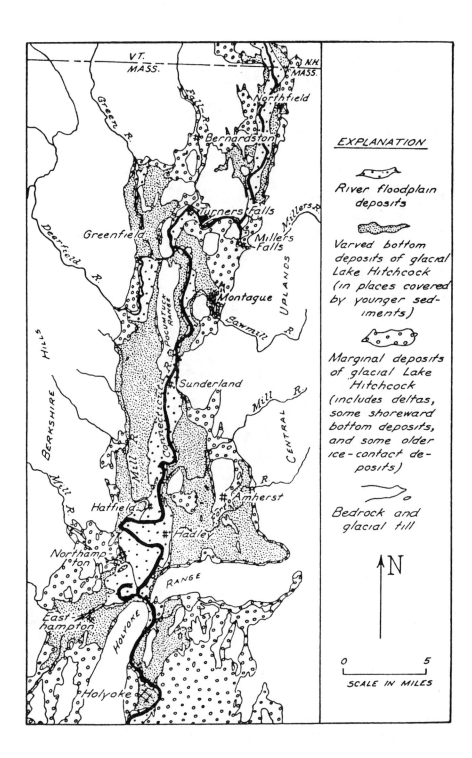

Figure 54 - Lake Hitchcock and postlake river deposits north of
the Holyoke Range (From Jahns, 1967).[12]

Figure 55 -

Varved clay lake bottom deposits of Lake Hitch-cock, Deerfield, MA.

Today, with the water drained, the flat delta tops are obvious geo-historical markers to the Hitchcock shoreline (Fig. 56). Plotting delta-top elevations reveals a strange fact. The lake shore is tilted! The smooth bedrock of the New Britain spillway is 72 feet above sea level, and delta-top elevations gradually increase northward at a rate of 4.2 feet per mile, four times steeper than the Connecticut River's slope! Did Lake Hitchcock flow like a rushing river? No. The tilted shoreline is a result of "postglacial rebound" after the lake drained. The crust, floating in the mantle like a ship in water, was depressed by the weight of its icy cargo. When melting removed the load, the land uplifted in proportion to the ice thickness. Since the ice thickness increased north-ward, so did rebound, leaving our northerly delta tops significantly higher (Fig. 57).

With Lake Hitchcock gone, the Connecticut River once again flowed across its valley, but the river inherited a landscape much different from preglacial times. Thick glacial and lake deposits buried the Con-necticut's preglacial, narrow bedrock channel, allowing the river to flow across its valley with greater freedom. Floodplains and waterfalls developed, setting the stage for the arrival of man.

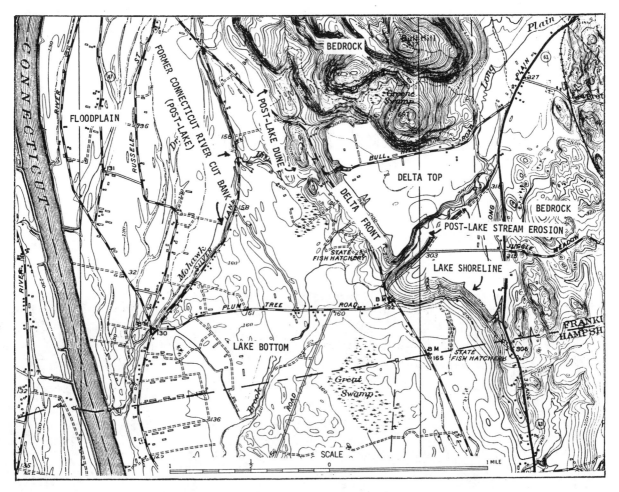

Figure 56 - Valley landforms as seen on a portion of the Mt. Toby topographic map (1955 edition).  Contour interval = 10 feet.

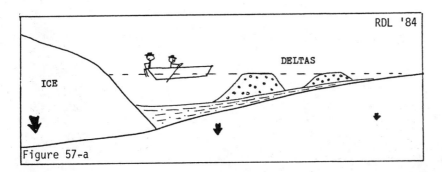

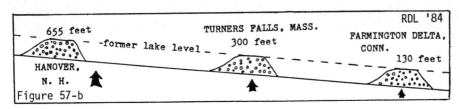

Figure 57 -
Glacial rebound and tilted deltas.
57-a - Deltas form while land is depressed by weight of ice (increasing to north).
57-b - After rebound (increasing to north), deltas and former lake surface tilted.  Drawing not to scale.  Arrows indicate relative amounts of depression (57-a) or rebound (57-b).

# PART FIVE

**Modern Times**

# MAN and ENVIRONMENT

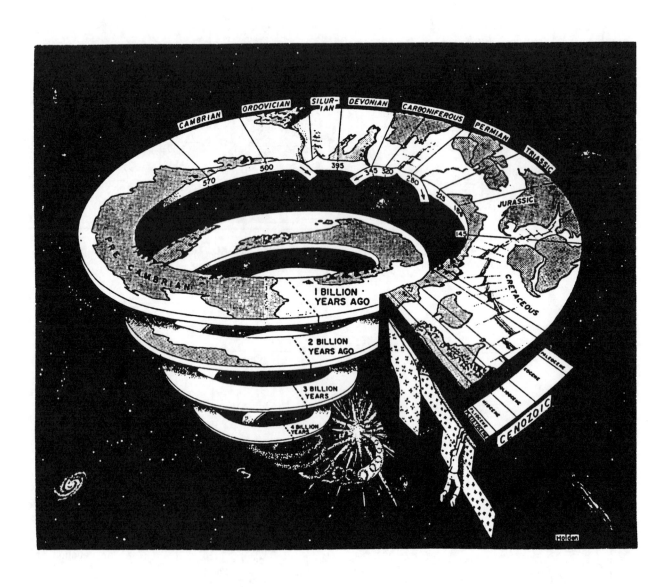

## ENTERING THE RECENT EPOCH OF GEOTIME

A fluvial orgy of erosion commenced with the draining of Lake Hitchcock.  Streams, unfettered by the lake level, flowed across the soft lake
sediments, actively eroding and creating prominent terraces and other landforms (Fig. 58).  Over 100 feet of sand, gravel, and varved clay have been
eroded by valley rivers.  Cut banks continue to eat into farmland, forest,
and occasional houselots as point bars build new beaches on inner river
bends.  Abandoned meanders document former river positions.  Their distinctive curving lakes or swamps are very important in the ecology of
the floodplain and are easily seen on topographic maps, or better yet,
from the vantage point of a scenic plane flight.

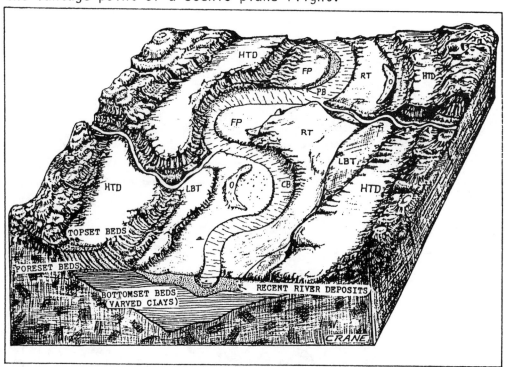

Figure 58 - Modern valley landforms.  HTD = High Terrace Delta, formed
            by Hitchcock delta tops; LBT = Lake Bottom Terrace, remnants
            of Hitchcock delta bottom; O = Oxbow Lake, river meander
            "cut-off"; CB = Cut Bank; RT = River Terrace, cut by mean-
            dering river when at former higher level; FP = Flood Plain,
            lowest river-formed terrace; PB = Point Bar.

Streams, evicted from their preglacial valleys by deposits of till,
deltas, and varved clay, created waterfalls, as Figure 59 illustrates.
Whether along the main stem of the Connecticut or along tributaries,
waterfalls are spectacular landscape aberrations and were important
sources of power for eighteenth and nineteenth century industrial development.  A hundred-foot "mini Niagara" existed upstream of Turners Falls,
Massachusetts, at the Barton Cove Nature Area, also the site of the famous dinoprint quarry.  As the Connecticut cut through the delta deposits
of the Millers River, it found itself on top of a ridge of sedimentary
rock that had been buried by the delta deposits.  The power of falling
water scoured two plunge pools into the bedrock before the river found a
channel through the obstruction.  The abandoned plunge pools, home of
legendary large bass, attract hopeful fishermen whose thoughts rarely

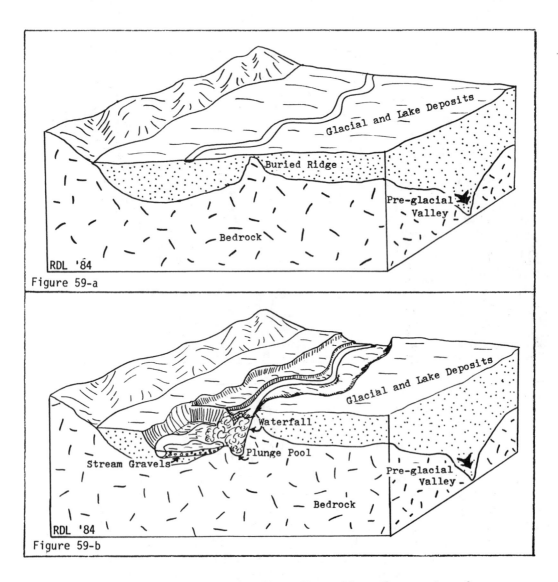

70

wander (unfortunately) back 10,000-12,000 years to when the Connecticut
thundered over the surrounding cliffs.

The draining of Lake Hitchcock left the barren, sediment-covered
lake floor at the mercy of the wind.  Clouds of dust blew out of the valley while sand piled up into dunes, some of which reach 50 feet high and
a mile long, "the most extensive inland dunes in New England"!  Most
dunes form smaller linear hills concentrated on the east side of the old
lake bottom by northerly and westerly winds.  Although now stabilized
by vegetation, if the botanic blanket is removed, perhaps by fire or
poor land use, the sands will continue their downwind migration.

Figure 59 - Development of waterfalls.  59-a - River flows on top of
            glacial and lake deposits.  59-b - Waterfall is created as
            stream erodes through the sediment cover to become super-
            imposed on bedrock outcrop.  Waterfalls at Barton Cove
            (now abandoned), Turners Falls, and Holyoke were created
            in this manner.

## PALEOINDIANS IN THE VALLEY

When did early people arrive in the Connecticut Valley? Did they camp and fish along the shores of Lake Hitchcock and swim in its icy waters? Evidence of Native Americans canoeing among Hitchcock's icebergs has yet to be found. "At present, all <u>unequivocal</u> evidence favors placing man's first entry into the Americas at about 13,000 to 12,000 B.P."[2](Before Present). Due to water storage in glacier ice, lower sea levels allowed animal herds and their hunters into the New World via the Alaska-Siberia "land bridge". Migration from this northern entry way (Fig. 60) theoretically would bring these hunter-gatherers into the valley area sometime before the lake drained, but the Hitchcock shoreline (so far) yields no evidence of contemperaneous Paleoindian occupation. Most Paleoindian sites are along the river-cut terraces of the lake floor, and since SCUBA was yet to be invented, these habitations must postdate Lake Hitchcock.

Figure 60 - Model for the migration of early humans into North America at the close of the Great Ice Age (From Matsch, 1976).[3]

A Paleoindian site 12,580 years old is found at Dutchess Quarry Cave, Orange County, New York, only 100 miles from the Connecticut Valley. Why then were Paleoindians not in the Connecticut Valley with Lake Hitchcock? The answer may lie with inaccuracy of the two radiocarbon dates for the lake's draining. These samples, analyzed

30 years ago, may have had some carbon weathered out during their years of burial in sandy soils, producing ages that are too young. University of Massachusetts anthropologists Mary Lou Curran and Dena Dincauze estimate "a reasonable drainage date for Lake Hitchcock no later than 12,900 B.P."[4] With the lake gone, rivers rapidly cut terraces in the soft lake deposits, and the region became much more habitable because of increased ecozone diversity (Table 3).

TABLE 3

| LANDFORMS, SOILS, AND VEGETATION OF OUR POSTLAKE CONNECTICUT VALLEY | | |
|---|---|---|
| Zones | Soils | Possible Vegetation |
| 1. Steep slopes, bedrock outcrops (35-90% grade) | Thin to no soil cover (till and bedrock) | Dwarf trees, lichens, shrubs, herbs, mosses, sedges (willow, birch, alder, bearberry) |
| 2. Less steep slope (15-25% grade) | Moderate to thin soils, often stony | Dwarf trees, shrubs, mosses, heath, plus scattered black spruce (birch, alder, juniper, bearberry) |
| 3. Late-glacial deltas | Soils high in gravel and sand | Dwarf willow, jack pine (possibly succeeded by spruce), woody shrubs, legumes (alder, bearberry) |
| 4. Floodplains and terraces | a. Sands and gravels<br>b. Silts | Sere<br>a. Barrens, quickly filling in with grasses, herbs<br>b. Many shrubs, then sedges, heath<br>c. More stable willow, alder thickets<br>d. Poplar (balsam), spruce on high river banks; open spruce woodland in areas protected from flood |
| 5. Lake sediments | a. Sands and gravels; postlake dunes<br>b. Clays, silts, sands | Shrubs, heath, jack pine (possibly succeeded by spruce)<br>Open woodland (black, white spruce, larch, moss, balsam fir, berries)<br>Open meadow (aspen, berries, jack pine, pulses, herbs, Artemesia) |
| 6. Bogs, shallow lakes, marshes, swamps | Muck | Dwarf trees, shrubs, sedges, moss, heath (black spruce, willow, alder, birch, Labrador tea, sphagnum, bilberry) |

(From Curran and Dincauze, 1977)[5]

The following legend may give some very tenuous support for early Indian witnesses to Lake Hitchcock in Massachusetts.

"A great Beaver supposedly lived in a great lake, and when his natural food supply became scarce, he strayed from the swamp and attacked men. The Indians grew angry and apprehensive and sought help from their Prince. The leader prayed to the god Manitou for help and then pursued the Great Beaver on a long chase. The Beaver was chased to the top of Mount Toby from which he plunged into the lake. From the top of Mount Toby, the Indian threw stones and dirt upon the giant animal and then jumped upon it and axed it. The great spirit Manitou was so pleased by the Indian's brave feat that he changed the Beaver into stone as a sign of approval to the tribe. Eventually the lake drained and disappeared completely and left the beaver - turned to stone - exposed: Mount Sugarloaf was the Beaver's sacred head;

the "Pocumtuck Range" was his body; and the lower hills
near the mouth of the Deerfield River were the Beaver's
tail."[5]

Unlike early people, plants and animals left a much clearer record
of their arrival. Pollen, deposited in kettle ponds and glacially
scoured lakes, documents the changing environment. For several thousand years, tundra grasses and sedges dominated the still-cold landscape. As the climate warmed and soils deepened, spruce, balsam fir,
and pine forests spread northward into the valley. Caribou herds
and elephantine woolly mammoths and mastodons inhabited the newly-
deglaciated land, and their bones and teeth are sometimes encountered
during excavation of peat bogs or even netted by fishermen from the
continental shelf, testimony to lower glacial-age sea levels.

## VALLEY RESOURCES

### soils

"A paradise" said many journals of early white settlers who, in the
1630s, entered our valley from the forested and stoney till soils of
eastern Massachusetts. Enticed by the tales of fur traders, new emigrants
navigated the shoals of Cape Cod and sailed upstream for 25 miles through
the Connecticut's "narrows" cut in metamorphic rock. Finally, they beheld
their goal, a wide valley with good water and fields already cleared by
the Indians! These rich floodplain lands were eagerly acquired from the
Indians, whose agricultural surpluses saved early colonists from starva-
tion several times.

Soils develop according to parent material, slope, climate, and time.
Glacial and fluvial processes have left us with a variety of parent materials
(bedrock, till, outwash, lake, and floodplain deposits) for new soil development. Table 4 summarizes valley soil types, uses, and hazards.

Our economy has diversified relative to that of our seventeenth century forebearers', and farming, an essential part of our economy and landscape, is being threatened by encroachment of "higher value" activities,
such as housing, shopping centers, etc. Our agricultural heritage should
be appreciated and supported, perhaps by zoning, preferred tax rates, and
purchase of land or easements. Agriculture is by far the best use of our
floodplains. It is important that we use them, not lose them.

### water

"Essentially, we have the same amount of water as the Pilgrims, except
that now there are 232 million of us using it."[1] And abusing it. Pollution
from a wide variety of sources increasingly threatens our water supplies, and
is one of our most pressing environmental concerns.

TABLE 4

| | | CONNECTICUT VALLEY SOILS AND SUBSOILS [6] | | |
|---|---|---|---|---|
| Landform | Major Soil Names | Formation and Characteristics | Uses | Potential Problems |
| Floodplain | Hadley Winooski Limerick | Silty flood deposits on varved clay, well-drained except in swampy, abandoned channels. | Best soils in the valley! Typical crops: shade tobacco, potatoes, onions, winter squash, carrots, cucumbers. | Encroachment of housing, wind and water erosion, especially gullies from uncontrolled runoff into major streams. |
| Terraces, Outwash Plains, Dunes | Hinkley Windsor Merrimack Ondawa | Stream deposits of gravel and sand composing kames, outwash plains, Hitchcock deltas, terraces, lake floor remnants, and wind-blown dune sand. | Housing, forests, dairy farms, local produce production, important groundwater recharge areas, and sand-gravel mining. | Leachate contamination of groundwater from septic systems and landfill waste disposal sites due to highly permeable soil and subsoil. Very droughty. |
| Ground Moraine, Drumlins, "Uplands" | Many | Surface cover of sandy, silty, gravelly till (ablation till) left on top of bedrock and dense, clay-rich till (lodgement or subglacial till; e.g., drumlins) as glacier melted. Commonly stoney, steep, and has variable thickness and composition. May have sandy-silty surface layer due to wind deposits as ice retreated, before vegetation was established. | Forests, housing, dairy farming, apple orchards, hay and pasture, landfill waste disposal site due to low permeability of subglacial till. | Cultivation and construction difficult due to thin and stoney soils. Subglacial till's low permeability creates drainage problems. Not suited for septic systems. |

Water is stored by geologic consent, and the Connecticut Valley has been generously provided for (Fig. 61). The 40-45 inches of yearly precipitation can either be trapped by damming the V-shaped valleys of unpolluted highland tributaries or tapped by wells drilled into porous aquifer zones bequeathed by the departed glacier. Exposed reservoirs can be easily monitored, but the groundwater system is much more complicated and is susceptible to serious contamination even before problems are recognized.

In the porous, sandy-gravelly deltas, kames, and outwash deposits which line the Connecticut and tributary valleys, all rainfall quickly penetrates into the groundwater system. These "recharge" areas are supremely important to the quantity and quality of groundwater. They also are very susceptible to pollution from such sources as gravel mining (abandoned pits are frequent sites of illegal hazardous waste), landfills (leachate), roads (salt -- over eight tons per lane-mile per year), agriculture (fertilizers and pesticides), and the many problems associated with industrial, retail, or residential development. It is essential to monitor recharge regions' groundwater and regulate land use to maintain water quality. "The extremely high cost of restoring contaminated waters to drinkable quality makes prevention of pollution the only practical course to protect...drinking water supplies."[8]

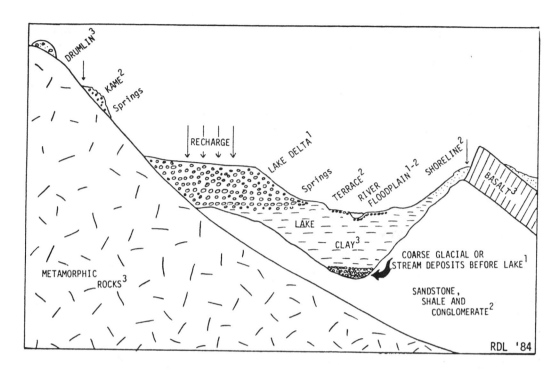

Figure 61 - Connecticut Valley groundwater potential. Class 1 - High yields,
100-200 gallons per minute (gpm) average with some wells yielding
1,000-2,000 gpm. Class 2 - Medium yields. Class 3 - Low yields,
5 gpm average with some wells exceeding 50 gpm in porous rock
zones (joints or faults). Arrows indicate major recharge areas.
"Lake Delta" and "Shoreline" refer to former Lake Hitchcock sediments.

We need to be aware of potential contamination sites in our communities. Be on the lookout for abandoned cans and barrels, rusting cars
leaking oil and coolant, seepage from underground storage tanks, salt
piles, and dumps, and notify your local board of health or state pollution
control agency (Table 5).

TABLE 5

STATE POLLUTION CONTROL AGENCIES

| Massachusetts | Connecticut |
|---|---|
| Dept. of Environmental Protection | Dept. of Environmental Protection |
| 436 Dwight St. | Water Resources Unit, Rm. 201 |
| Springfield, Mass. 01103 | State Office Building |
| | Hartford, Conn. 06106 |
| (413) 784-1100 | (203) 566-7220 |

Household products also present risks. Waste oil, paint, solvents, pesticides and their used containers, and cleaners for drains, ovens, metals, etc., are disposal problems. Waste oil can be recycled at many service stations or recycling centers, but disposal of other products adds more poisons to landfill leachate. If flushed down the drain, they will move even quicker than leachate into groundwater or streams. The only solution is a safe regional hazardous waste disposal site, combined with more effective local solid waste disposal techniques, such as incineration and recycling.

## 'minerals'

### sand and gravel

The voluminous delta deposits of Lake Hitchcock and other glacial lakes provide the valley's most important geologic resource in terms of tonnage and income. The gravel is used as fill, or sorted into various sizes for concrete, leach fields, and road sand.

The people of Turners Falls, Massachusetts, and vicinity learned much about groundwater when a plan was revealed to ship nearby delta gravel 100 miles to Boston in return for railcars of metropolitan garbage. A grassroots effort successfully educated the public and elected officials about the environmental importance of these "pine barrens", the county's major groundwater recharge area. In the near future, our sand and gravel resources will very likely be in demand by the expanding coastal "megalopolis". Using 70-ton capacity railcars, Boston Sand and Gravel Company currently imports gravel from central New Hampshire, 110 miles away.

While many deltas can survive decades of mining, some landforms can vanish in a matter of days. Eskers, curving ridges of ice-bound stream deposits (see Fig. 47-a and 47-b) have excellent quality gravel. However, due to their small size and value as a scenic landform revealing a glimpse into the meltwater history of the glacier, they should be preserved. We are not going to get new ones for quite some time!

### clay

The quiet bottom waters of glacial lakes provided the "habitat" for thick varved clay, both in Lake Hitchcock and farther south in the Quinnipiac River Valley. The clay was mined for brickmaking, formerly a common valley industry. Brickyards diminished as demand fell and fuel costs for baking rose. Only a few operations remain, such as at Windsor Locks and Hampden and at Suffield, Connecticut, where Jurassic red shale is quarried and crushed for brick raw material.

### crushed stone

After sand and gravel, trap rock is our most important geologic resource. Trap makes an ideal aggregate, being hard yet easily cracked into blocky pieces because of cooling joints. Uses include bituminous aggregate and beds for highways and railroads, for which it has been shipped over 1,000 miles beyond the valley.

Besides local effects, such as noise, dust, and blasting, the quarries have minor environmental impact. Although an eyesore to some, geologists dream about newly blasted exposures with their potential treasures: crystals formed by groundwater seepage into cracks and gas bubbles. Connecticut Valley trap is widely known for its beautiful and sometimes rare mineral specimens. Crystals of quartz, amethyst, datolite, prehnite, calcite, and epidote are rather commonly found. Rare members of the zeolite minerals are sometimes collected as well as crystals of black babingtonite, the Massachusetts state mineral.

### building stone

In the mid nineteenth century, quarries in our valley sandstones employed thousands of workers to mine and shape the brown or red stone of the Portland Formation (Fig. 62). The colorful sandstone was de-

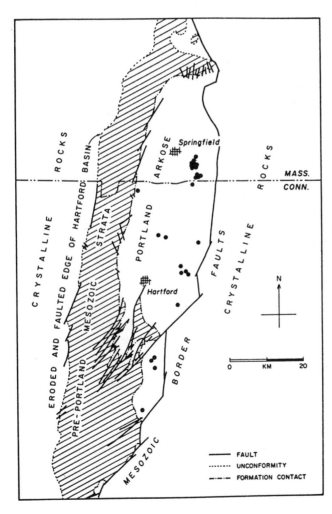

Figure 62 - Location of brownstone quarries in the Portland Formation in the Connecticut Valley (From Hubert, et al, 1982).

posited as Jurassic stream floods left sandy sediment at the margin of
alluvial fans.  Cheaper construction materials, such as concrete, displaced brownstone's popularity, and the quarries have been abandoned
to the seepage of groundwater.  Too bad.  The mining produced beautiful
stone, and miners occasionally disinterred dinobones and prints.

### other mineral resources

Gene Kennedy, known as the "Old Prospector", has panned flakes and
small nuggets of gold from tributary streams in the northern Connecticut
Valley, but previous generations of fortune hunters, seeking copper and
lead ores touted by speculators, invested much more than Mother Nature
ever refunded.  Gold was scraped by the glacier from unknown Vermont
locations and deposited in till.  Today's streams eroded the till and
concentrated the high-density gold in their stream deposits.  Do not
be fooled by yellow, iron-stained mica flakes!  If they are really gold,
flakes will be maleable, nonelastic, and dense.

Lead occurs in veins along faults north and west of the Holyoke
Range.  Sparkling, cubic galena crystals were an important source of
lead for bullets during the Revolutionary War when our European supplies were cut off, but concentrations of galena proved limited and
uneconomical.

America's first mining company was organized in 1706 to work copper
deposits in the East Granby, Connecticut, area (Fig. 63), and between
1729 and 1739, Connecticut copper was used in the first coins minted
in America.  However, like lead, limited concentrations resulted in finan-
cial failure.  The main "benefit" of the mining came between 1773 and
1827 when the mine and workings became the infamous Newgate Prison, today
a historic site.

Both the lead and copper ores formed as hot, mineral-rich fluids
seeped along faults and through sedimentary formations, precipitating their
metals and associated minerals.  Similar events can be seen today in the
fault zones of the Mojave Desert.  Just where the minerals came from remains a mystery.  Although the copper deposits are definitely localized
near the Talcott lavas, the lavas themselves have a "conspicuous absence
of copper-bearing minerals."

Although the ores were unproductive, the mine "dumps" are -- for the
mineral collector.  Abundant and diverse accessory minerals can still be
found as coatings and crystals amid the mine tailings despite previous
generations of salvagers.

### energy

"Turners Falls, the Home of White Coal" exclaimed a 1912 ad publiciz-
ing the copious energy to be harvested from frothing waterfalls, products
of glacial-induced drainage changes (see Fig. 59).  In the beginning, the
falling water pushed waterwheels, with great belts transferring the turn-

ing power to mill machinery producing flour, lumber, paper, guns, tools, and other commodities. Dams raised water levels for better "head" and canals provided a wider area for mills to capture the water power. Today, the falling waters turn turbines, providing electricity to commercial and residential users throughout the valley and beyond.

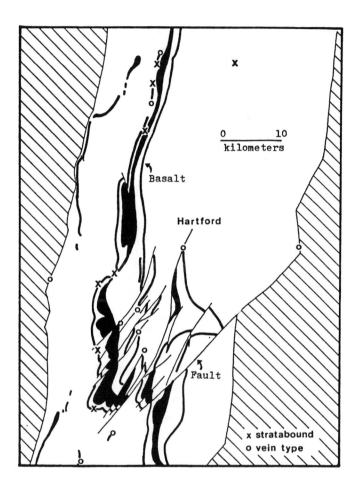

Figure 63 - Distribution of copper occurrences in the Connecticut Valley (From Gray, 1982)."

River water is important for power production even if it does not "fall". The Yankee nuclear plants in Haddam, Connecticut, and Vernon, Vermont, suck in river water at rates of several hundred thousand gallons per minute for reactor cooling and steam condensation, and the heated water is returned to the river with minimal environmental impact. Conventional fossil fuel plants also utilize the river's cool waters, but in lesser amounts.

At Northfield, Massachusetts, an unconventional but increasingly popular hydrologic scheme uses river water to create electricity during high demand periods. Using excess electricity generated during nights and weekends, large turbine pumps push river water up 800 feet to a mountaintop reservoir. During power production, the stored water rushes through the pressure shaft, turns the turbines, and returns to the river through the tailrace tunnel (Fig. 64). The four turbines have one million kilowatts of short-term generating power, twice the output of the Haddam nuclear plant.  The river's level fluctuates several feet during these cycles, resulting in some riverbank  erosion, certainly less environmental impact than building and operating fossil fuel or nuclear plants to provide this energy.

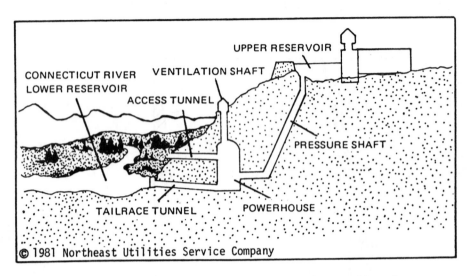

Figure 64 - Diagram of Northfield Mountain Project.  Water is pumped from the Connecticut River into the large storage reservoir on top of Northfield Mountain. When electricity is needed, the water flows from the reservoir through the generators in the powerhouse and back into the Connecticut River (From Sammartino, 1981).[5]

Fossil fuels in the valley?  An exploration company has recently purchased drilling rights to a thousand acres in Granby, Massachusetts, hoping that there may be enough decomposed organics in buried Mesozoic lake sediments to provide a source of natural gas, or perhaps oil. Coal, oil, and natural gas are found in the larger Mesozoic valleys farther south, so the potential is here.  The expensive process of well drilling is an essential step in evaluating possible productivity in the Connecticut Valley.

## GEOHAZARDS

### floods

"As the flood waters spill over the banks of the river, the floodplain actually becomes part of the river. Seasonal spring flooding is important to the maintenance of the fertility of the floodplain soils.  When the water flows onto the floodplain, it slows down and drops its load of new, fertile soil onto the land.  In return, the flood waters pick up decaying plant material, which is then transported downstream and provides food for river animals.

In addition, flood waters are vital to the water supply. These waters seep into the ground and help re-fill underground water reserves, called aquifers.

Small, temporary floodplain pools are refilled each spring. A variety of small, young animals, such as tad-poles and young insects..., are supported by the pools. These animals then form a necessary link in the overall food chain of the flood plain."[12]

We pay a high price for trespassing on the flood's plain, as evidenced by the disastrous floods of 1936 and 1938. Since then, the Corps of Engineers has spent $600 million (all figures in 1984 dollars) building flood control dams and dikes (Table 6) to protect valley residents, and it is comforting to know that a repetition of the 1938 flood would be 90% less damaging. The Corps calculates that these flood control projects have prevented an estimated $470 million in damages, but the Connecticut and its tributaries still cause $30 million in annual damage.[13]

TABLE 6

| CORPS OF ENGINEERS FLOOD CONTROL MEASURES [13] | | | | | |
|---|---|---|---|---|---|
| Reservoir | River | Date Completed | Drainage Area (sq.mi.) | Flood (in.) | Storage (ac.ft.) |
| Surry Mountain (NH) | Ashuelot | 1941 | 100 | 5.9 | 31,200 |
| Birch Hill (MA) | Millers | 1941 | 175 | 5.3 | 49,900 |
| Knightville (MA) | Westfield | 1941 | 162 | 5.7 | 49,000 |
| Tully (MA) | E. Br. Tully | 1949 | 50 | 8.3 | 22,000 |
| Union Village (VT) | Ompompanoosuc | 1950 | 126 | 5.6 | 38,000 |
| Otter Brook (NH) | Otter Brook | 1598 | 47 | 7.0 | 17,600 |
| Barre Falls (MA) | Ware | 1958 | 55 | 8.2 | 24,000 |
| No. Springfield (VT) | Black | 1960 | 158 | 5.9 | 49,500 |
| No. Hartland (VT) | Ottauquechee | 1961 | 220 | 6.0 | 70,000 |
| Ball Mountain (VT) | West | 1961 | 172 | 6.0 | 54,600 |
| Townshend (VT) | West | 1961 | 106 | 5.8 | 32,800 |
| Mad River (CT) | Mad | 1963 | 18.2 | 10.0 | 9,700 |
| Littleville (MA) | W. Br. Westfield | 1965 | 52.3 | 8.2 | 23,000 |
| Conant Brook (MA) | Conant Brook | 1966 | 7.8 | 9.0 | 3,740 |
| Colebrook River, CT) | W. Br. Farmington | 1970 | 118 | 8.0 | 50,200 |
| Sucker Brook (CT) | Sucker Brook | 1970 | 3.4 | 8.1 | 1,480 |
| | | Total Area: | 1,571.0 | Total Storage: | 526,702 |

Living alongside a bubbling brook is much more hazardous than along the mighty Connecticut. Due to their smaller channel capacities, tributaries flood with greater frequency, and there is little or no warning. When excessive tributary flow puts the Connecticut over its banks, the flood crest advances like a slow-moving, wide swell, predictable and publicized.

Flooding results from a variety of events (Table 7) of which spring snow melt and hurricanes are the most threatening. Seven lower mainstem cities (Hartford, East Hartford, Springfield, West Springfield, Chicopee, Holyoke, and Northampton), being located at least partly on the floodplain, are the major areas at risk. To tame floods, "big dams are still the best solution," says the Corps.[13] However, due to expense, environmental impact, and the fact that we have 16 flood control dams already, it is unlikely that more will be built. Nonstructural measures, such as education, relocation of at-risk structures, regulation of floodplain land use, maintenance of agriculture, and land acquisition for open space are much more cost effective in keeping people away from floods. Other flood damage reduction measures include: preserving natural flood storage areas (do not fill and develop oxbows and floodplains!), improving flood warning and emergency response systems, and raising existing dikes protecting major cities rather than building new flood control structures.

"We must recognize that the 'problem' exists because we created it. And the 'solution' will come about because we reach a reasoned accommodation with those aspects of the river's drainage function that can be harmful. If it's a question of whose fault it is, we don't have the river to blame. We have ourselves to blame."[13]

### landslides

Everyone knows how slipery wet clay is, so it should come as no surprise that varved clays of valley lowlands as well as clay-rich till of the surrounding highlands have high slide potential on steep and moderate slopes. Curving scars with lumpy "toe" deposits at their base mark the sites where gravity overpowered internal friction, moving the mass a little closer to the center of the earth. Engineers constantly aid gravity's battle with clay as almost any construction site or road cut will verify. Occasionally, houses are built on unstable slopes. They have nice views but serious foundation problems.

Construction on the flat slopes of floodplains or former lake beds are subject not to slippage, but to differential compaction. Many a once-flat parking lot has become cracked and "rolling", with adjacent buildings exhibiting lesser symptoms of the same disease (due to their foundation support).

In combating these hazards, one must realize the inherent instability of clay-rich soils, and that adding weight, water, or increasing the slope of these soils promotes movement. These problems could be much worse. Clays deposited under sea water have a vastly greater instability. Known as "quick clays", they can liquify by vibrations of earthquakes, pile-drivers, and even highway traffic, and have created disastrous flows in Alaska and the St. Lawrence Valley.

TABLE 7

## FLOODS

| Main Cause | Contributing Factors | Results | Example |
|---|---|---|---|
| Spring Snowmelt | Rain, frozen ground (no percolation), dormant vegetation (limited transpiration) | Tributary and mainstem flooding, ice adds to abrasion power and can form secondary dams at river bends. | Mid March, 1936 - 4-6" rain accompanied by 2 weeks of melting produced the Connecticut Valley's greatest flood. River flow reached 238,000 cfs (cubic feet per second) (average annual flow is about 11,000 cfs) at Turners Falls. Extensive flooding, bank erosion, bridge washouts, property damage. |
| Tropical Storms (hurricanes) | Saturated soil (no percolation) | Tributary and mainstem flooding | Mid September, 1938 - Wet month (over 12" of rainfall), soils saturated, hurricane winds uproot great numbers of trees, river crests at 186,000 cfs at Turners Falls, MA. Record flooding in Vermont and New Hampshire tributaries, second largest Connecticut River flood. |
| Ice Dams | Flooding in early spring stacks thick tributary and mainstem ice where river channel is narrow or obstructed | Ice lodges in narrow or obstructed parts of channel and grows larger as more ice becomes trapped behind original blockage. Water is backed up causing upstream flooding. When dam breaks, the backed up water can cause some downstream flooding. | Many local examples |
| Dam Failure | Poor design and maintenance, flooding | Major, unpredicted flooding of downstream lowlands | May, 1874 - Nation's first major dam failure. Mill River Dam, 3 miles above Williamsburg, MA, washed out, releasing one billion gallons at 60,000 cfs, killing 144 in Williamsburg, Leeds, and Haydenville. |
| Thunderstorms | Intense rainfall localized over a small drainage basin | Tributary flooding in affected drainage basin, usually no flood warning, locally very damaging. Mainstem, because of greater capacity, does not flood. | Many local examples |

## earthquakes

Although it has been about 140 million years since the Eastern Border Fault sent major shock waves across the region, reminders of geo-restlessness are still common (Fig. 65 and Table 8). The strange Moodus Seismic Area, a few miles east of Portland, Connecticut (Fig. 66), is "one of the most continuously seismically active places in the northeastern United States."[14] Quakes have been noted to be heard and not felt! Indians named this hilly region "Morehemoodus", meaning "place of noises", where could be heard the voice of Mother Nature or confrontations between Indian and white gods. The confrontations continue. Beginning in 1980, earthquake "swarms" of a few hundred events each (most detectable only by instruments) have occurred several times, and the area's pulse is now monitored by seismographs anchored in bedrock.[14]

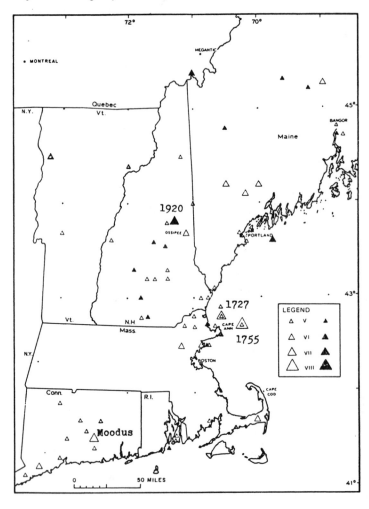

Figure 65 -
Locations of the New England earthquakes greater than IV on the Modified Mercalli Scale. Size of the symbol indicates intensity of the earthquake. An open symbol indicates that the location was based on historical data. A solid symbol indicates that the location was determined instrumentally (From Simmons, 1977).[15]

Figure 66 - Historical seismicity of Connecticut.[14] The symbols show the maximum modified Mercalli intensity for the events. O = III, △ = IV, □ = V, ● = VI, and ■ = VII.

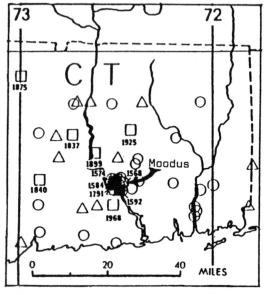

The Moodus area's extraordinary activity is due to its geology, one of the most complex in New England. Episodes of faulting and folding date from Late Precambrian to post-Jurassic, and stress is still stored in rocks. Blasting and rock excavation, like a cathartic massage, allow rock stress to release and can result in the formation of small faults.

The most damaging New England quakes of 1727, 1755, and 1940 are associated with now-solid granite intrusions that pushed their way through surrounding rocks about 110 million years ago. Stress builds because these intrusions grade from granite at the surface to gabbro (dense, "black granite") at depth, each having different "elastic" properties. Over 200 years have passed since the Boston area quakes. During that period, the city expanded onto filled marshland and bays, extremely unstable soil. The stage is set for catastrophe. Consider the events of 1755:

> "Upon the first shock of the earthquake, many persons jumped out of their beds, and ran immediately into the streets, while others sprung to the windows, trembling, and seeing their neighbors as it were naked, shrieked with the apprehension of its being the day of judgment, and some thought they heard the last trumpet sounding, and cried out for mercy; others fainted away with the fright, and those of the most composed temper, that were sensible of these tremendous shakings, expected instantly to be swallowed up and buried in the ruins. In short, children ran screaming to their parents to save them, and the brute creatures lowed and ran to the barns for protection; the dogs howled at their master's door; the birds fluttered in the air with a surprise, and all the animal creation were filled with terror, and never was such a scene of distress in New England before. In my walk out about sunrise, every face looked ghastly, and many persons' knees smote one against another..."[16]

Fortunately, most of the Connecticut Valley is far from significant quake sources, and safe, although the earthwaves will rock us, particularly in areas of clay-rich soils.

TABLE 8

| MODIFIED MERCALLI INTENSITY SCALE | |
|---|---|
| I. Not felt except by a very few under specially favorable circumstances. | VIII. Damage slight in specially designed structures; considerable in ordinary, substantial buildings, with partial collapse; great in poorly built structures. Panel walls thrown out of frame structures. Fall of chimneys, factory stacks, columns, monuments, walls. Heavy furniture overturned. Sand and mud ejected in small amounts. Changes in well water. Persons driving motorcars disturbed. |
| II. Felt only by a few persons at rest, especially on upper floors of buildings. Delicately suspended objects may swing. | |
| III. Felt quite noticeably indoors, especially on upper floors of buildings, but many people do not recognize it as an earthquake. Standing motorcars may rock slightly. Vibration like passing of truck. Duration estimated. | IX. General panic. Damage considerable in specially designed structures; well-designed frame structures thrown out of plumb; great in substantial buildings with partial collapse. Buildings shifted off foundations. Ground cracked conspicuously. Underground pipes broken. |
| IV. During the day, felt indoors by many, outdoors by few. At night, some awakened. Dishes, windows, doors disturbed; walls make creaking sound. Sensation like heavy truck striking building. Standing motorcars rocked noticeably. | X. Some well-built wooden structures destroyed; most masonry and frame structures destroyed with their foundations; ground badly cracked. Rails bent. Landslides considerable from river banks and steep slopes. Shifted sand and mud. Water splashed (slopped) over many banks. |
| V. Felt by nearly everyone, many awakened. Some dishes, windows, etc. broken; a few instances of cracked plaster; unstable objects overturned. Disturbances of trees, poles, and other tall objects sometimes noticed. Pendulum clocks may stop. | |
| VI. Felt by all, many frightened and run outdoors. Some heavy furniture moved; a few instances of fallen plaster or damaged chimneys. Damage slight. | XI. Few, if any, (masonry) structures remain standing. Bridges destroyed. Broad fissures in ground. Underground pipelines completely out of service. Earth slumps and land slips in soft ground. Rails bent greatly. |
| VII. Everybody runs outdoors. Damage negligible in buildings of good design and construction; slight to moderate in well-built ordinary structures; considerable in poorly built or badly designed structures; some chimneys broken. Noticed by persons driving cars. | XII. Damage total. Waves seen on ground surfaces. Lines of sight and level distorted. Objects thrown upward into air. |

# PART SIX

# the GEOLOGICAL FUTURE

# THE PAST IS THE KEY TO THE FUTURE

"Some say the world will end in fire,
some say in ice."

Robert Frost

A crucial yet uncontrolled experiment is being played out on earth. Doubling every 35 years, expanding human populations gobble resources in pursuit of that energy-intensive cultural "high" known as Western Civilization. Results of these pursuits can be seen even in rural areas -- pollution. While smog and water pollution have great local impact, carbon dioxide will colorlessly and odorlessly effect great geologic changes on the face of the earth. Released by combustion of wood and fossil fuels, atmospheric $CO_2$ will double in about 60 years, increasing worldwide average temperatures 1-5° C due to the "greenhouse effect"! While warmer temperatures may moderate our high winter energy costs, their cumulative impact is to melt glacial ice. Releasing Antarctic and Greenland meltwater to the sea could raise sea levels two feet by 2040, greatly increasing coastal erosion and flooding. If all the world's ice melts, sea levels will rise (over several thousand years) almost 200 feet, resulting in critical losses of floodplain farmland, mass inland migration, and competition for decreased continental living space. In the Connecticut Valley, all major cities will be abandoned as saltwater penetrates as far as the future metropolis of Greenfield, Massachusetts. Our basalt ridges will become picturesque islands in the productive waters of the "Connecticut Bay".

However, no geologist believes that our climatic rollercoaster ride of the past 2 1/3 million years is finished (Fig. 67). Interglacials of about 10,000 years alternate with longer-lasting glacial ages, and we are due for a change since the last glacial ice melted from New England about 10,000 years ago. Noted geologist John Imbrie of Brown University predicts that as fossil fuels are depleted over the next few centuries, the $CO_2$-inspired "super interglacial" will disintegrate into the next ice age about 2,000-3,000 years hence. Although a major ice advance will spell doom for the Connecticut Valley, the world will actually be more hospitable than one might believe. Deserts, now cooler and wetter, will bloom and develop beautiful lakes in their basins. World sea levels will recede, revealing a fertile continental shelf for habitation (once the salt is flushed out by rainfall).

Further into the mists of geotime, far beyond the boundaries of millenia, the earth's rhythm will be uninterrupted by the superficial scratchings of rivers, glaciers, or man. The earth's internal heat will propel crustal plates across the globe at rates of inches per year, amounting to 20 to 100 miles in a million years. Because of changing mantle convection, the Atlantic may start to shrink over the next several hundred million years. Subduction zones may develop, giving the east coast an appearance like the Pacific Northwest, a place of spectacular volcanoes and earthquakes. This will be just the beginning. As subduction swallows ocean crust, Europe and Africa will once again collide with the Americas, creating the New Appalachians along the continental boundaries (Fig. 68). The valley area will be safe from these tectonic transformations, being several hundred miles from the continent's edge.

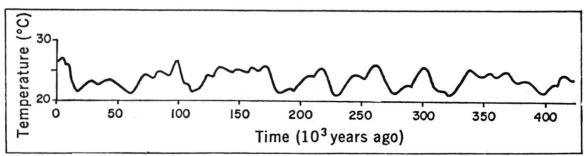

Figure 67 - Generalized ocean paleotemperatures as determined from
sediment core samples (From Emiliani, 1970)?

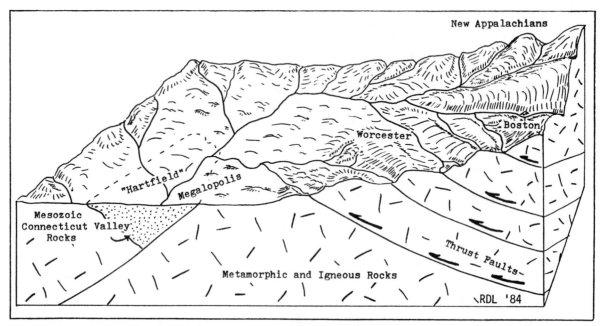

Figure 68 - Possible future topography of Connecticut Valley region.
Boston would be abandoned as a major metropolis in favor
of safer foothill communities such as Hartford, Connecticut, and Springfield, Massachusetts, now "Hartfield".
Europe and Africa would be located east of the New Appalachian Range.

So, beyond the more immediate threat of climate instability, the
future looks quite promising for the Connecticut Valley.  We will inhabit
the foothills of a great new range of mountains linking us to other crustal
plates perhaps as extensive as Pangaea; there will be a new world for
the descendants of genus Homo.

# APPENDICES, REFERENCES, AND SUGGESTED READINGS

## APPENDIX

APPENDIX I

CONNECTICUT VALLEY ROCK IDENTIFICATION CHART

| | | |
|---|---|---|
| **I G N E O U S** | FORMATION | MOLTEN ROCK (magma) which cooled either <u>FAST</u> (lava) or <u>SLOWLY</u> (granites) |
| | LOOK FOR | 1.  RANDOM arrangement of minerals (if large enough to be seen)<br>2.  MASSIVE, HARD ROCKS |
| | COMMON ROCKS | LAVA (Basalt) - very small minerals (may be too small to see), found in our valley ridges<br>GRANITE - easily seen minerals, interlocking texture, found in the highlands |
| **S E D I M E N T A R Y** | FORMATION | ERODED PIECES OF ROCK:  gravel, sand, mud; now cemented into rock |
| | LOOK FOR | 1.  ROUNDED GRAINS (sand, pebbles)<br>2.  LAYERING (bedding)<br>3.  "STRUCTURES" - ripples, mud cracks, fossils |
| | COMMON ROCKS (found throughout the valley) | CONGLOMERATE - former gravel<br>SANDSTONE - our variety called ARKOSE due to presence of many "weak" minerals such as feldspar<br>SHALE - former mud<br>LIMESTONE, DOLOMITE - Calcium-rich mud of lakes; found in thin, light-colored layers |
| **M E T A M O R P H I C** | FORMATION | HEAT, PRESSURE, CHEMICALLY ACTIVE FLUIDS due to mountain building or nearby igneous intrusions |
| | LOOK FOR | 1.  "FLOWAGE" BANDING composed of <u>light</u> or <u>dark</u> minerals, therefore, not similar to sedimentary layering<br>2.  "NEW" MINERALS - garnets, mica, pyrite |
| | COMMON ROCKS (found in the highlands) | GNEISS ("nice") - banded light and dark minerals<br>SCHIST - shiny, mica-rich<br>SLATE - formerly shale but now harder, no sedimentary structures<br>MARBLE - formerly limestone, usually light colored, calcite prominent, will not scratch glass<br>QUARTZITE - formerly sandstone, usually light colored with "frosty" appearance; very hard rock, will easily scratch glass<br>METACONGLOMERATE - pebbles stretched by metamorphism |

SAMPLE COLLECTING ETIQUETTE

1.  If you think you have found something unique or rare, DO NOT HAMMER or REMOVE.  Sketch or photograph and contact a geologist to evaluate the find.  Many geological features can be rendered almost useless if removed.

2.  Do not trespass, litter, or knock down fences and stone walls!  Many interesting geologic sites have been closed due to inconsiderate collectors.

3.  Good collecting sites are a valuable and limited resource.  Be conservative in your collecting.

## APPENDIX II

### SOURCES OF GEOLOGIC INFORMATION

A.  MAPS

1.  Topographic Maps ("Quadrangles")

    These maps are essential for locating cultural features such as
    towns, roads, trails, and political boundaries as well as rivers,
    mountains, and other landforms.  They can be obtained locally,
    usually at selected book or stationery stores.  See map (page
    94  ) for quadrangle names.

2.  Geologic Quadrangle Maps

    There are two varieties of geologic maps.  Surficial geologic
    maps deal with the origin and location of surface deposits,
    mostly resulting from glacial and river processes.  Bedrock
    geologic maps ignore the surface deposits and analyze the
    origin and characteristics of the bedrock.  Sometimes a map
    incorporates both surficial and bedrock data and is simply
    termed a geologic map.  All varieties of geologic maps have
    a wealth of data, and a written report accompanies each map.
    See page  94  for listing of available geologic maps in the
    Connecticut Valley area and Section D for addresses.

3.  State Geologic Maps

    The long-awaited Bedrock Geologic Map of Massachusetts is now
    available from the U.S. Geological Survey.  For about $10, one
    receives a multicolored display of rock types, cross sections,
    and structural analysis, as well as formation names, ages and
    descriptions, and references.  See U.S. Geological Survey ad-
    dress on next page.  Connecticut's newly published, full-color
    geologic map is available from the State Geological and Natural
    History Survey.  See next page for address.

B.  EDUCATIONAL INSTITUTIONS

The Connecticut Valley possesses an abundance of excellent secondary
schools, colleges, and universities.  The colleges and universities
often offer courses concerning our valley geology, and faculty at
all levels are usually excellent resource people for individual con-
sultations or group presentations.  Libraries are indispensable information centers housing books, theses, maps, and periodicals.

C.  NATURE CENTERS, STATE PARKS, MUSEUMS, AND OTHER ORGANIZATIONS

Many private groups, public agencies, and even businesses are involved
in the preservation and interpretation-education of our scenic and geologic resources.  Support these important organizations by visiting,
learning, enjoying, and joining!


D.  IMPORTANT ADDRESSES FOR OBTAINING MAPS AND OTHER INFORMATION
    (See map, page 94 , for map numbers)

    1.  For ordering U.S. Geological Survey materials:

            Eastern Distribution Branch
            U.S. Geological Survey
            1200 South Eads Street
            Arlington, VA  22202

    2.  For Connecticut Geological and Natural History Survey
        publications:

            Connecticut Department of Environmental Protection
            Publications and Sales
            165 Capitol Avenue, Room 555
            Hartford, CT    06106

        Ask for their catalog, "Natural Resources Information
        Directory and List of Publications", an important
        information source.

## EXPLANATION OF "VALLEY AREA GEOLOGIC MAPS"

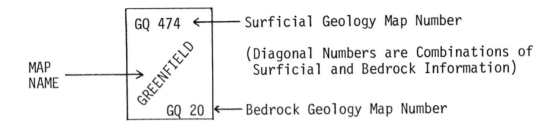

MAP NAME → GQ 474 ← Surficial Geology Map Number

(Diagonal Numbers are Combinations of Surficial and Bedrock Information)

GREENFIELD

GQ 20 ← Bedrock Geology Map Number

## KEY TO ABBREVIATIONS

GQ MAPS:  Geologic Quadrangle Maps, published by U.S. Geological Survey

OF MAPS:  Open-File Maps, not formally published but available from:

> Open-File Services Section
> Western Distribution Branch
> U.S. Geological Survey
> Box 25425
> Federal Center
> Denver, CO  80225

Prices vary.

QR MAPS:  Quadrangle Report of Connecticut Geological and Natural History Survey

IP:  Mapping or Publication In Progress

## Pertinent References

B =  Balk, R., "Geology of the Mt. Holyoke Quadrangle, MA," Geological Society of America Bulletin   v. 68, (1957) 481-504.

H =  Hinthorne, J., "Bedrock Geology of the Mt. Tom Area, MA," MS Thesis, University of Massachusetts (Amherst), 1967.

L =  Larsen, F., "Surficial Geology of the Mount Tom Quadrangle, MA", Ph.D. Thesis, University of Massachusetts (Amherst), 1972.

N =  Norton, S., "Geology of the Windsor Quadrangle, MA", U.S. Geological Survey Open File Report, 1967.

## VALLEY AREA GEOLOGIC MAPS

| | | | | | |
|---|---|---|---|---|---|
| GQ 642<br>NORTH ADAMS<br>GQ 139 | ROME<br>GQ 642 | HEATH<br>GQ 735 | GQ 82<br>COLRAIN<br>GQ 86 | IP<br>BERNARDSTON<br>GQ 90 | GQ T440<br>NORTHFIELD<br>GQ 92 | GQ 4<br>MT. GRACE<br>GQ 3 |
| WINDSOR<br>N | PLAINFIELD<br>GQ 877 | IP<br>ASHFIELD<br>OF 855 | GQ 116<br>SHELBURNE FALLS<br>GQ 87 | GQ 474<br>GREENFIELD<br>GQ 20 | IP<br>MILLERS FALLS<br>GQ 93 | IP<br>ORANGE<br>OF 77-788 |
| IP<br>PERU<br>OF 74-93 | WORTHINGTON<br>GQ 857 | GOSHEN<br>GQ 1561 | GQ 80<br>WILLIAMSBURG<br>GQ 85 | GQ 9<br>MT. TOBY<br>GQ 8 | OF 78-285<br>SHUTESBURY | IP<br>QUABBIN RES. |
| OF 1967<br>BECKET<br>OF 74-92 | CHESTER<br>GQ 858 | IP<br>WESTHAMPTON | IP, L<br>EASTHAMPTON<br>H | MT. HOLYOKE<br>B<br>H | OF 77-63<br>BELCHERTOWN | IP<br>WINSOR DAM |
| OTIS<br>OF | BLANDFORD<br>GQ 1312 | IP<br>WORONOCO | IP, L<br>MT. TOM<br>H | IP<br>SPRINGFIELD N<br>H | IP<br>LUDLOW<br>GQ 1353 | GQ 1465<br>PALMER<br>OF 76-489 |
| IP<br>TOLLAND<br>CENTER | W. GRANVILLE<br>OF 78-271 | GQ 891<br>SOUTHWICK | GQ 892<br>WEST<br>SPRINGFIELD | SPRINGFIELD S<br>GQ 678 | OF 71-73<br>HAMPDEN | GQ 1429<br>MONSON |
| | GQ 1170 | GQ 537 | | GQ 1368 | GQ 1374 | |
| GQ 871<br>WINSTED<br>IP | NEW<br>HARTFORD<br>GQ 1257 | GQ 798<br>TARIFFVILLE<br>GQ 370 | GQ 137<br>WINDSOR LOCKS<br>GQ 388 | GQ 965<br>BROAD BROOK<br>GQ 434 | ELLINGTON<br>QR 4 | GQ 1216<br>STAFFORD SPRINGS<br>OF |
| GQ 939<br>TORRINGTON<br>QR 25 | OF<br>COLLINSVILLE<br>QR 16 | GQ 147<br>AVON<br>GQ 134 | HARTFORD<br>NORTH<br>GQ 223 | MANCHESTER<br>GQ 433 | ROCKVILLE<br>QR 6 | SOUTH COVENTRY<br>OF |
| GQ 984<br>THOMASTON<br>IP | GQ 145<br>BRISTOL<br>IP | GQ 119<br>NEW BRITAIN<br>GQ 494 | QR 20<br>HARTFORD<br>SOUTH<br>IP | GQ 1354<br>GLASTONBURY<br>QR 5 | GQ 1504<br>MARLBOROUGH<br>GQ 791 | IP<br>COLUMBIA<br>GQ 592 |
| WATERBURY<br>QR 22 | GQ 146<br>SOUTHINGTON<br>QR 200 | GQ 150<br>MERIDEN<br>GQ 738 | IP<br>MIDDLETOWN<br>QR 8 | IP<br>MIDDLE HADDAM<br>OF | GQ 1205<br>MODUS<br>QR 27 | COLCHESTER<br>QR 27 |
| QR 35<br>NAUGATUCK<br>QR 9 | QR 12<br>MOUNT CARMEL<br>GQ 199 | QR 10<br>WALLINGFORD<br>OF | GQ 756<br>DURHAM<br>QR 37 | QR 36<br>HADDAM<br>QR 13 | GQ 1370<br>DEEP RIVER<br>QR 19 | HAMBURG |
| QR 23<br>ANSONIA<br>GQ 426 | QR 18<br>NEW HAVEN | QR 14<br>BRANFORD<br>IP | QR 28<br>GUILFORD<br>IP | QR 28<br>CLINTON<br>QR 29 | QR 31<br>ESSEX<br>QR 15 | QR 31<br>LYME<br>QR 21 |
| QR 23<br>MILFORD<br>GQ 427 | QR 18<br>WOODMONT | | | | | |

0     10     20 MILES

# APPENDIX III

## ILLUSTRATIONS OF CONNECTICUT VALLEY

## MESOZOIC ANIMALS

Reproduced from R. S. Lull, 1953
Triassic Life of the Connecticut Valley (Revised), Bulletin 81
Connecticut Geological and Natural History Survey

*Gigandipus caudatus* E. Hitchcock. A carnosaurian dinosaur based upon the trackway after Hitchcock. Proportions modified from *Teratosaurus* after V. Huene. One-fortieth natural size. One of the largest of the Connecticut valley forms with a possible length of twenty or more feet.

*Selenichnus falcatus* E. Hitchcock. Based upon trackway by Lull. A small cœlurosaurian dinosaur. Proportions suggested by *Saltopus* after V. Huene. One-fourth natural size.

*Otozoum moodii* E. Hitchcock. Based on the trackway by Hitchcock. A large prosauropod dinosaur. Suggested by *Plateosaurus* except for the fore feet which are less prehensile. Possibly of plant feeding habits. One thirty-second natural size. Overall length of animal about twenty feet. The so called flange or web described by Hitchcock is interpreted as a wave of mud displaced by the animal's weight.

*Hyphepus fieldi* E. Hitchcock. Based upon trackway by Lull. A small cœlurosaurian dinosaur, possibly web-footed. Proportions suggested by the thecodont *Saltoposusuchus* after V. Huene. One-eighth natural size.

*Yaleosaurus* (*Anchisaurus*) *colurus* (Marsh). Restoration of skeleton.
One-twelfth natural size. After Marsh.

*Arachnichnus dehiscens* E. Hitchcock. Quadrupedal reptile based on the trackway by Lull, one-half natural size.

*Comptichnus obesus* E. Hitchcock. A small quadrupedal reptile, based upon the trackway by Lull. The bulk of the weight is borne on the stubby toed feet, only the tips of the digits of the small hand impressing as though the creature were rising to a bipedal gait. In many instances the hand does not impress at all. One-half natural size.

*Sustenodactylus curvatus* (E. Hitchcock). A primitive quadrupedal reptile. Restoration suggested by the contemporaneous *Hypsognathus* of New Jersey. Trackway by Lull, one-half natural size.

*Sauropus barrattii* (E. Hitchcock). Based upon the trackway after Hitchcock. An ornithopod dinosaur. Proportions suggested by those of *Hypsilophodon* except for the elongation of the tarsus. One-sixteenth natural size. The interpretation of this animal as an Ornithischian is largely influenced by the small *Camptosaur*-like hands which are devoid of grasping claws. Osseous remains of Ornithischia are as yet unknown from the Triassic. Interpreted as a plant-feeding animal with a length of about six feet.

*Batrachopus deweyi* (E. Hitchcock). A quadrupedal reptile probably allied to *Stegomosuchus*. A thecodont reptile of the suborder Pseudosuchia, one-fourth natural size.

*Ammopus marshi* Lull. Based upon the trackway after Lull. A small quadrupedal form of unknown affinity. Restored as somewhat lizard-like in appearance, one-fourth natural size.

*Cheirotheroides pilulatus* E. Hitchcock. A quadrupedal pseudosuchian reptile allied to *Stegomosuchus*. One-half natural size.

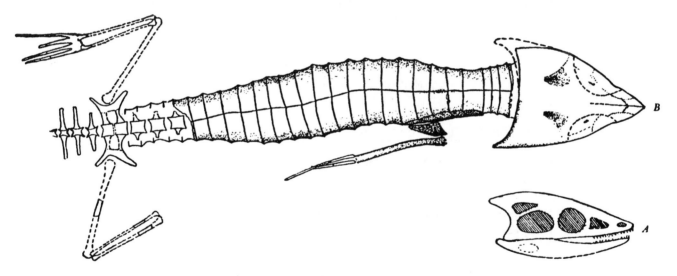

*Stegomosuchus longipes* (Emerson and Loomis). Natural size. After Emerson and Loomis. A. Right side view of skull. B. Dorsal view of head and body.

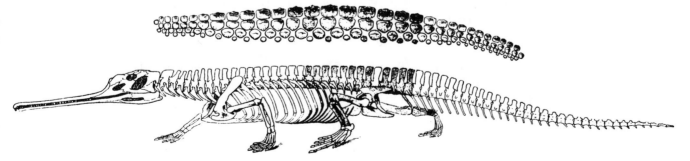

Skeleton of the phytosaur *Clepsysaurus manhattanensis*, from von Huene after Matthew. The shaded parts are those preserved in the Fort Lee specimen

# REFERENCES AND SUGGESTED READINGS

## Part I  Introduction

1. Krynine, P., 1950, Petrology, Stratigraphy, and Origin of the Triassic Sedimentary Rocks of Connecticut:  Conn. Geol. and Nat. Hist. Surv. Bull., No. 73, 247 p.

2. McPhee, J., 1980, Basin and Range:  Farrar Straus Giroux Publishers, N.Y., 216 p.
   A field trip through geological time and space by a master writer.  Relates the formation of the Connecticut Valley to the Mojave Desert's "Basin and Range" structure.

3. Powell, J., 1875, Exploration of the Colorado River, U.S. Government Printing Office, Washington, D.C.

4. Tollo, R., and Nicholson, S., 1979, Introductory Physical Geology Field and Laboratory Exercises:  Univ. of Mass., Amherst,  153 p.  Drawing from the cover, by Marie Litterer.

For more information regarding rocks, minerals, or geohistory, many excellent basic textbooks are available.  The "old faithful" Golden Guide to Rocks and Minerals is a must for every beginner regardless of age.

## Part II  From Sea to Supercontinent:  The Paleozoic Era

1. Larsen, E., and Birkeland, P., 1982, Putnam's Geology:  Oxford Univ. Press, N.Y., 789 p.  Drawing from p. 704.

2. Scotese, C., Bambach, R., Barton, C., Van Der Voo, R., and Ziegler, A., 1979, Paleozoic Base Maps:  J. Geol., Vol. 87, 217-277.

3. Robinson, P., and Hall, L., 1980, Tectonic Synthesis of Southern New England, in Wones, D., ed., The Caledonides in the USA:  I. G. C. P. Project 27:  Caledonide Orogen, 1979 Meeting, Blacksburg, VA:  VA Polytechnic Inst. and State Univ. Memoir, No. 2, p. 73-82.
   The best attempt at integrating plate tectonics theory into the complex geology of southern New England.

4. Stearn, C., Carroll, R., and Clark, T., 1979, Geological Evolution of North America:  J. Wiley & Sons, N.Y., 565 p. Drawing from p. 434, based on the work of Chadwick and Cooper.

5. Hubert, J., Reed, A., Dowdall, W., and Gilchrist, J., 1978, Guide to the Mesozoic Redbeds of Central Connecticut: Guidebook No. 4, Conn. Geol. and Nat. Hist. Surv., Hartford, 129 p. Drawing from p. 31.

Because metamorphism has greatly obscured the true histories of colliding plates in the northern Appalachians, new interpretations are sure to be proposed. Stay tuned.

Part III   The Mesozoic Era:   Creation and Destruction of the Connecticut Valley

1. Hubert, J., Reed, A., Dowdall, W., and Gilchrist, J., 1978, Guide to the Mesozoic Redbeds of Central Connecticut: Guidebook No. 4, Conn. Geol. and Nat. Hist. Surv., Hartford, 129 p. Map from p. 4.

2. Krynine, P., 1950, Petrology, Stratigraphy, and Origin of the Triassic Sedimentary Rocks of Connecticut: Conn. Geol. and Nat. Hist. Surv. Bull., No. 73, 247 p.

3. Weddle, T., and Hubert, J., 1983, Petrology of Upper Triassic Sandstones of the Newark Supergroup in the Northern Newark, Pomeraug, Hartford, and Deerfield Basins: Northeastern Geol., Vol. 5, p. 8-22.

4. Bain, G., and Meyerhoff, H., 1976, The Flow of time in the Connecticut Valley: Conn. Valley Hist. Mus., Springfield, MA, 168 p.

5. Little, R., 1982, Lithified Armored Mud Balls of the Lower Jurassic Turners Falls Sandstone, North-Central Massachusetts: Jour. Geology, Vol. 90, p. 203-207.

6. Chandler, W., 1978, Graben Mechanics at the junction of the Hartford and Deerfield basins of the Connecticut Valley, MA: Contrib. no. 33, Dept. of Geol. and Geog., Univ. of MA, Amherst, 151 p.  See Table 1 for compilation of timing of valley events during the Mesozoic.

7. Brophy, G., Foose, R., Shaw, F., and Szekely, T., 1967, Triassic geologic features in the Connecticut Valley near Amherst, MA: in Robinson, P., ed., New England Intercollegiate Geological Conference Guidebook, 1967 annual meeting, Amherst, MA, p. 61-72.      This guidebook is a great resource for the northern valley area. Includes road log for field trips.

8. "Fire Under the Sea", a 20-minute, 16 mm film, available from Moonlight Productions, Mountain View, Cal.

9. Tollo, R., and Nicholson, S., 1979, Introductory Physical Geology Field and Laboratory Exercises: Univ. of Mass., Amherst, 153 p.  Drawing from the cover, by Marie Litterer.

10. Gray, N., 1982, Mesozoic Volcanism in North-Central Connecticut: in Joesten, R., and Quarrier, S., eds., Guidebook for field trips in Conn. and So. Central MA: Guidebook No. 5, CT Geo. and Nat. Hist. Surv., Hartford, CT, p. 173-194. Excellent resource book for mid-valley area. Includes road logs.

11. Deane, J., 1861, Ichnographs from the sandstone of the Connecticut River: Little, Brown and Co., Boston, 61 p., 46 plates. Quote from p. 8.

12. Hitchcock, E., 1858, Ichnology of Massachusetts: W. White, State Printer, Boston, 205 p., 60 plates. Quote from p. 196.

13. Ibid, p. 4.

14. Colbert, E., 1970, Fossils of the Connecticut Valley - The Age of Dinosaurs Begins (Revised Ed.), CT Geol. and Nat. Hist. Surv., Bull. 96, 32 p. See p. 7.

15. Hitchcock, E., 1858, see p. 198.

16. Hitchcock, E., 1865, Supplement to the Ichnology of New England, Wright and Potter, State Printers, 96 p., 20 plates. Quote from p. 33.

17. Hitchcock, E., 1858, see p. 190.

18. Ostrom, J., 1968, Geology of Dinosaur Park, Rocky Hill, Connecticut: in Orville, P., ed., New England Intercollegiate Conference Guidebook, Guidebook No. 2, CT Geol. and Nat. Hist. Surv., Hartford, CT, p. 1-12 (c-3).

19. Mossman, D., and Sargeant, W., 1983, The footprints of extinct animals: Scientific American, Vol. 244, p. 75-85.

20. Ostrom, J., 1972, Were some dinosaurs gregarious?: Palaeogeog. Palaeoclim. Palaeoecol., Vol. 11, p. 287-301.

21. McDonald, N., 1982, Paleontology of the Mesozoic rocks of the Connecticut Valley: in Joesten, R., and Quarrier, S., eds., Guidebook for field trips in Conn. and So. Central MA: Guidebook No. 5, CT Geo. and Nat. Hist. Surv., Hartford, CT, p. 143-172. Quote from p. 150.

22. Emmerson, B., 1898, Geology of Old Hampshire County (Franklin, Hampshire and Hampden Counties), Gov't. Printing Office, Washington, D.C., 790 p. Quote from p. 347-348.

23. Cornet, B., Traverse, A., and McDonald, N., 1973, Fossil spores, pollen, and fishes from Connecticut indicate early Jurassic age for part of the Newark Group: Science, Vol. 182, p. 1243-1247.

24. Colbert, E., 1968, Men and Dinosaurs:  E.P. Dutton and Co., N.Y., 281 p.  See p. 4.

25. Simon, C., 1984, Mass Extinctions and Sister Stars:  Science News, Vol. 125, p. 116.

26. Allaby, M., and Lovelock, J., 1983, The Great Extinction: Doubleday and Co., Garden City, N.Y., 182 p.  Quote from p. 168.

Guidebooks are excellent sources for up-to-date information, including bibliographies, for further research.  The three most useful for valley information are listed above (see #1, #7, and #10).  The following book is an excellent overview of dinosaur information: McGowan, C., 1983, The Successful Dragons:  S. Stevens Co., Toronto, Canada, 263 p.  Also see Johansson, W., 1952, A bibliography to the Paleontology of Massachusetts, 1821-1949, Special Publ. #3, Univ. of MA, Dept. of Geology and Geography, Amherst, MA.

## Part IV  The Cenozoic:  Rebirth of the Valley

1. Waley, A., 1935, The way and its power:  Houghton Mifflin Co., Boston, 262 p.  Quote from p. 238.

2. Rahn, P., 1971, Weathering of tombstones and its relationship to the topography of New England:  Jour. of Geol. Education, Vol. 9, p. 112-118.

3. Deane, R., 1967, The surficial geology of the Hartford South quadrangle:  Conn. Geol. and Nat. Hist. Surv., Quadrangle Report No. 20, Hartford, CT, 43 p., Map.

4. Matsch, C., 1976, North America and the great ice age: McGraw-Hill, 131 p.  Quote from p. 1.

5. Curran, M., and Dincauze, D., 1977, Paleoindians and paleolakes:  New data from the Connecticut drainage: Annals of the N.Y. Acad. of Science, Vol. 288, p. 333-348.  Quote from p. 347.

6. Larsen, F., and Hartshorn, J., 1982, Deglaciation of the southern portion of the Connecticut River Valley of Massachusetts:  in Larson, G., and Stone, B., eds., Late Wisconsin glaciation of New England:  Kendall/Hunt Pub. Co., Dubuque, Iowa, p. 115-128.

7. Koteff, C., and Pessl, F., 1981, Systematic ice retreat in New England:  U.S. Geol. Surv. Prof. Paper 1179, 20 p.

8. Hartshorn, J., and Colton, R., 1967, Geology of the southern part of glacial Lake Hitchcock and associated deposits:  in Robinson, P., ed., Guidebook to field trips, New England Intercollegiate Geological Conference, Amherst, MA, p. 73-88.

9. Ashley, G., 1972, Rhythmic sedimentation in glacial Lake Hitchcock, Massachusetts-Connecticut: Contrib. No. 10, Dept. of Geol. and Geogr., Univ. of MA, Amherst, 148 p.

10. Antevs, E., 1922, The recession of the last ice sheet in New England: Amer. Geogr. Soc. Res. Ser. No. 11, 120 p.

11. Flint, R., 1956, New radiocarbon dates and late-Pleistocene stratigraphy: Amer. Jour. Sci., Vol. 254, p. 265-287.

12. Jahns, R., 1967, The Late Pleistocene of the Connecticut Valley in northern Massachusetts: in Robinson, P., ed., Guidebook to field trips, New England Intercollegiate Geological Conference, Amherst, MA, p. 166-193.

Other interesting references are:

"Glacier on the Move", an 11 min., 16mm film using time-lapse photography to illustrate glacial motion and moraine development. Available from Encyclopaedia Britannica Educational Corp., 425 North Michigan Avenue, Chicago, Ill. 60611.

Denny, C., 1982, Geomorphology of New England, U.S. Geol. Surv. Prof. Paper 1208: U.S. Gov't. Printing Office, Washington, D.C., 18 p. Good overview of recent work. Includes extensive bibliography.

Davis, M., 1969, Climatic changes in southern Connecticut recorded by pollen disposition at Rogers Lake: Ecology, Vol. 50, p. 409-422. Very interesting and complete analysis of the many vegetation changes since the ice age.

Part V  Modern Times:  Man and Environment

1. Schafer, J., and Hartshorn, J., 1965, The Quaternary of New England: in Wright, H., and Frey, D., eds., The Quaternary of the United States: Princeton Univ. Press, New Jersey, p. 113-128. Quote from p. 124.

2. West, F., 1983, The antiquity of man in America: in Wright, H., ed., The Late Pleistocene, Vol. 1: Univ. of Minn. Press, Minneapolis, MN, p. 364-382. Quote from p. 378.

3. Matsch, C., 1976, North America and the great ice age: McGraw-Hill, 131 p.

4. Curran, M., and Dincauze, D., 1977, Paleoindians and paleo-lakes: New data from the Connecticut drainage: Annals of the N.Y. Acad. of Sci., Vol. 288, p. 333-348. Quote from p. 347.

5. Sammartino, C., 1981, The Northfield Mountain Interpreter: Northeast Utilities, Berlin, CT, 160 p.
   An excellent guide to our history and natural history. Available from the Northfield Mt. Environmental Center, Rt. 63, Northfield, MA 01360.

6. Mott, J., Fuller, D., Filios, F., and Hotz, C., 1967, Soil Survey of Franklin County, Massachusetts: U.S. Dept. of Agriculture, Soil Conservation Service, U.S. Gov't. Printing Office, Washington, D.C., 204 p., Maps.

7. Brinkley, David, 1983, News report quoted in Introduction of Water 2000, an inventory and assessment of water needs through the year 2000: Lower Pioneer Valley Regional Planning Commission Report, 203 p.

8. Massachusetts Department of Environmental Quality Engineering, 1983, Groundwater Protection Strategy, 12 p. brochure.

For more information on valley groundwater, consult:

Cederstom, D., 1967, Groundwater in the Connecticut Valley of Massachusetts: in Farquhar, O., ed., Economic Geology in Massachusetts: Univ. of Mass. Graduate School, Amherst, MA, p. 477-486.
    Although some deglaciation events at odds with
    current interpretations, this is an excellent
    summary of how our valley aquifers developed.

Cushman, R., 1964, Groundwater resources of north-central Connecticut: U.S. Geol. Surv. Water Supply Paper 1752, 96 p.

9. Hubert, J., Gilchrist, J., and Reed, A., 1982, Jurassic redbeds of the Connecticut Valley: in Joesten, R., and Quarrier, S., eds., Guidebook for field trips in Connecticut and south-central Massachusetts: New England Intercollegiate Geological Conference, Guidebook No. 5, Conn. Geol. and Nat. Hist. Surv., Hartford, CT, p. 103-142.

10. Bain, G., and Meyerhoff, H., 1976, The Flow of Time in the Connecticut Valley: Conn. Valley Hist. Mus., Springfield, MA, 168 p. See p. 73.

11. Gray, N., 1982, Copper occurrences in the Hartford Basin of northern Connecticut: in Joesten, R., and Quarrier, S., eds., Guidebook for field trips in Connecticut and south-central Massachusetts: New England Intercollegiate Geological Conference, Guidebook No. 5, Conn. Geol. and Nat. Hist. Surv., Hartford, CT, p. 195-208.

Regarding our petroleum potential, the oil companies have good reason to evaluate the Mesozoic rift valleys. See Zeigler, D., 1983, Hydrocarbon potential of the Newark Rift System, Eastern North America: Northeastern Geology, Vol. 5, p. 200-208.

12. Goldberg, T., 1979, Marshes and Meanders - the story of the Connecticut River: Amherst, MA, Mass. Public Interest Research Group.

13. New England River Basins Commission, 1976, The river's reach, a unique program for floodplain management in the Connecticut River Basin: N.E.R.B.C., 292 p.  See pages 8, 15, and 77.

14. Barosh, P., London, D., and de Boer, J., 1982, Structural geology of the Moodus Seismic Area, south-central Connecticut:  in Joesten, R., and Quarrier, S., eds., Guidebook for field trips in Connecticut and south-central Massachusetts: New England Intercollegiate Geological Conference Guidebook No. 5, Conn. Geol. and Nat. Hist. Surv., Hartford, CT, p. 419-437.

15. Simmons, G., 1977, Our New England Earthquakes: Weston Geophysical Corp., Westboro, MA, 12 p.

16. Holmes, Dr., quoted in White, H., 1843, The early history of New England illustrated by numerous interesting incidents:  I.S. Boyd Publisher, Concord, N.H., p. 52.

## Part VI  The Geological Future

1. Baes, C., Goeller, H., Olson, J., and Rotty, R., 1977, Carbon dioxide and climate:  the uncontrolled experiment: American Scientist, Vol. 65, p. 310-321.

2. Emiliani, C., 1970, Pleistocene Paleotemperatures:  Science, Vol. 168, p. 822-824.

## Addendum to References:  The Latest Connecticut Valley Guidebook

Tracy, R. J., ed., 1985, Guidebook For Fieldtrips in Connecticut and Adjacent Areas of N.Y. and R.I., Guidebook #6, Conn. Geological and Natural History Survey, Dept. of Environmental Protection; 588 p.